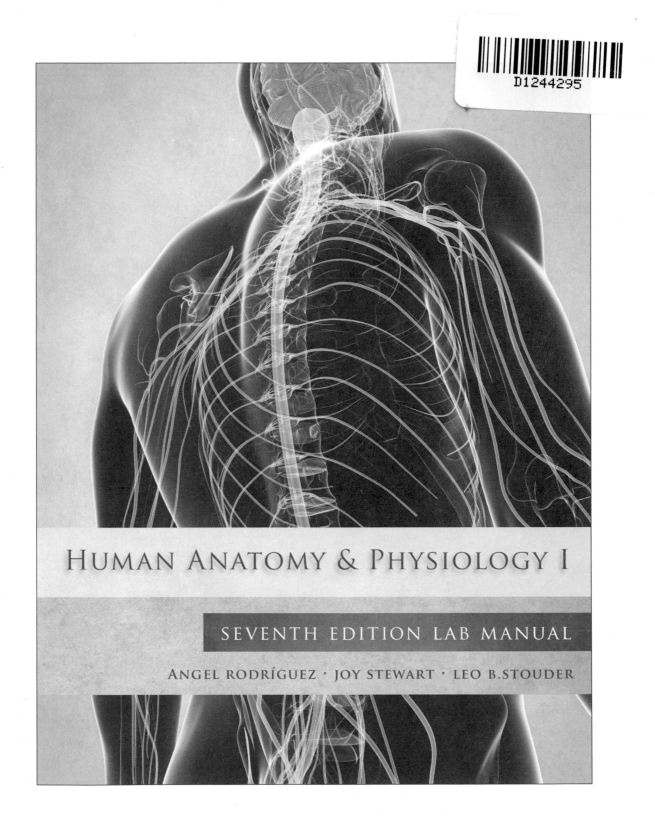

Human Anatomy & Physiology I

SEVENTH EDITION LAB MANUAL

Angel Rodríguez · Joy Stewart · Leo B. Stouder

bluedoor
small publishing done big®

Chief Executive Officer: Jon K. Earl

President, College: Lucas Tomasso
President, Private Sector: Dawn Earl
Regional Manager: Greg Bartell

Business Development Coordinator: Jennifer Smith

Senior Production Manager: Connie Dayton
Production Manager: Dan Woods
Production Manager: Amber Wahl
Production Manager: Julianne Prior-Miller
Assistant Production Manager: Ben Sweeney
Production Manager: Stephanie Larson
Project Manager: Peggy Li

Consulting Editors: Bruce D. Wingerd, M.S.
                     Suzanne S. Frucht, Ph.D.
                     Anna M. Kats, M.S., Florida Atlantic University
                     Michelle F. Cavallo, M.S., Florida Atlantic University
                     John F. Wiginton, Ph.D., University of Mississippi
                     Stephanie R. Dillon, Ph.D., Florida State University

Cover Design: Julianne Prior-Miller

ISBN-13: 978-1-59984-738-2

Published by bluedoor, LLC
              10949 Bren Road East
              Minneapolis, MN 55343-9613
              800-979-1624
              www.bluedoorpublishing.com

Printed in the United States of America.
10 9 8 7 6 5 4 3 2 1

About the Authors

Professor Angel Rodríguez

Professor Rodriguez graduated Magna Cum Laude with a Bachelor's degree in Marine Biology. He has a Master's degree in Biological Oceanography and an Ed. D. from the University of Florida (UF), in Educational Leadership with a concentration in Higher Education. Dr. Rodriguez has been teaching for over twenty years and has won every award that can be given from Professor of the year to being awarded the distinguished Motorola Corporation Endowed Teaching Chair. Among his many accomplishments, Professor Rodriguez has been accredited with saving the Plain Pigeon of Puerto Rico from extinction.

Professor Joy Stewart

Professor Stewart has a Bachelor of Science Honors Degree, a Master's degree in Biological Sciences, and an Ed. D. in Curriculum and Instruction. Dr. Stewart's teaching experience extends from Jamaica to Florida and spans approximately 30 years. She motivates her students by saying, "Students who work hard in college are guaranteed academic success!"

Professor Leo Stouder

Professor Stouder has a Bachelor's degree in Human Biology and a Doctoral degree in Chiropractic Medicine. Dr. Stouder has practiced chiropractic medicine for over 25 years and has been teaching at Broward College for over 15 years. Dr. Stouder is certified in both Human Dissection and Acupuncture. He's quoted as saying, "That means I'm qualified to stick sharp objects in both living and dead people."

Table of Contents

1

Fundamentals

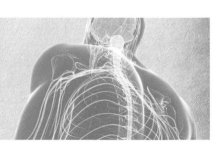

OBJECTIVES:

After completing this laboratory you should be able to perform tasks listed below.

1. Demonstrate knowledge of laboratory safety and procedural rules.
2. Use directional terms properly.
3. Use appropriate terms to describe planes and the location of all the abdominal regions of the human body.
4. Measure and use the correct metric units to record i) linear measures, ii) volumes, iii) mass, and iv) temperature.

A. Laboratory Safety and Procedural Rules

Activity 1.1: Studying Laboratory Safety and Procedural Rules

1. Note the location of the safety eyewash station, fire extinguisher, fire blanket, first aid kit, biohazard waste container, broken glass container, and the emergency gas and water shut off in the laboratory.
2. Do not enter the laboratory without the supervision of an instructor.
3. Do not bring food or drinks into the laboratory.
4. Smoking is prohibited.
5. Always wear protective coats in the laboratory.
6. Wear disposable gloves, and safety glasses when performing activities that involve the use of hazardous materials.
7. Secure long hair, loose clothing, and jewelry for your personal safety.
8. Keep all equipment away from the edge of your laboratory tables.
9. Properly dispose of waste material as directed by your instructor.
10. Inform your instructor immediately about all spills, accidents, or damaged equipment.
11. Use a disinfectant to decontaminate tables after completion of your laboratory activities.
12. Wash your hands with soap and warm water before leaving the laboratory.

B. Directional Terms

Directional terms refer to the relative location of body parts to each other.

Activity 1.2: Studying Directional Terms

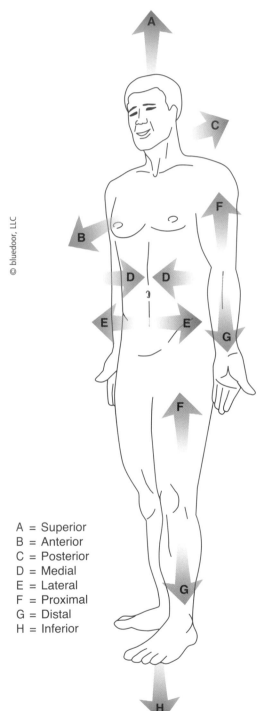

Observe Figure 1.1 and study the meaning of the directional terms included on Table 1.1.

© bluedoor, LLC

A = Superior
B = Anterior
C = Posterior
D = Medial
E = Lateral
F = Proximal
G = Distal
H = Inferior

Figure 1.1: Directional terms

Table 1.1: Directional Terms

Directional Terms	Meaning
Superior	Above
Inferior	Below
Anterior	In front
Posterior	Behind
Medial	Toward the midline
Lateral	Toward the side
Bilateral	On both sides
Ipsilateral	On the same side
Contralateral	On opposite sides
Proximal	Closer to the trunk of the body
Distal	Further from the trunk of the body
Superficial	At or near the surface
Deep	Inside the body, away from the surface

C. Planes

Planes divide the body or organs and produce surfaces called **sections**.

Activity 1.3: Studying Planes

Observe Figure 1.2 carefully and note the effect of cutting the body along the sagittal, transverse, and coronal (frontal) planes.

- **Sagittal (Median) planes** produce left and right sides and produce sagittal sections.
- **Midsagittal planes** divide the body or organs into two equal parts.
- **Parasagittal planes** divide the body or organs into two unequal parts.
- **Transverse (horizontal) planes** divide the body or organs into superior and inferior parts and produce transverse or cross sections.
- **Coronal (frontal) planes** divide the body or organs into anterior and posterior parts and produce frontal sections.

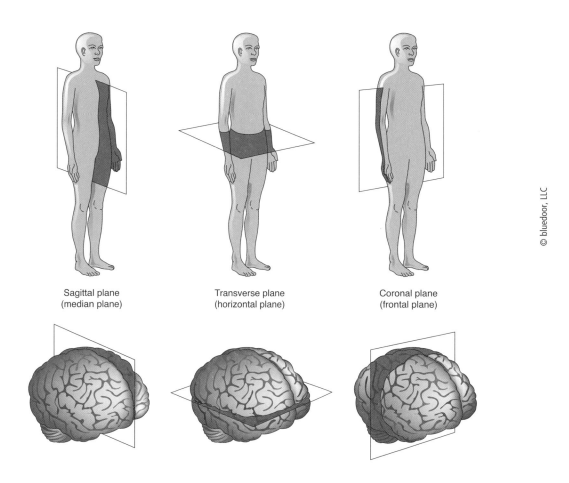

Sagittal plane
(median plane)

Transverse plane
(horizontal plane)

Coronal plane
(frontal plane)

Figure 1.2: Planes of the human body

D. Abdominopelvic Regions

Anatomists divide the abdominopelvic region of the body into nine regions. From top right to lower left these regions are **right hypochondriac**, **epigastric**, **left hypochondriac**, **right lumbar**, **umbilical**, **left lumbar**, **right inguinal**, **hypogastric**, and **left inguinal**. However, clinicians usually divide the body's abdominopelvic region into four quadrants: the right upper quadrant; left upper quadrant; right lower quadrant; and left lower quadrant that are referenced in relation to abnormalities or disorders.

Activity 1.4: Locating Abdominopelvic Quadrants

Study Figure 1.3 carefully. Then, locate the four abdominopelvic quadrants on a human torso model.

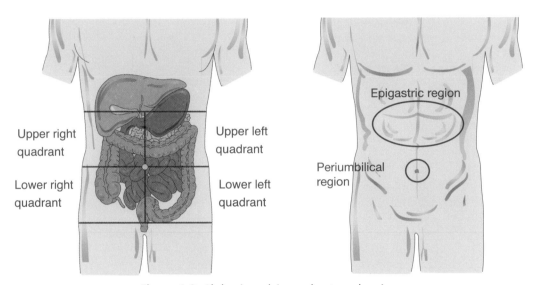

Figure 1.3: Abdominopelvic quadrants and regions

E. Measurements

Measurements allow scientists to communicate with each other about the results of quantitative experiments. The **metric system** is used universally for scientific communication that involves measurements. This system is based on units of 10. Therefore, it is easy to convert from one metric unit to another. Each unit of 10 indicates length, or volume (how much), or mass (how much matter) on a scale of 1 to 100.

Activity 1.5: Studying the Metric System

1. Examine the large poster in your lab that illustrates the metric system.
2. Use a meter ruler to measure the length of your upper limb and the span of your hand.
3. Record your answer in the space provided.

My upper limb measures:    The span of my hand is:

_____.   _____.

Remember: The standard metric unit of length is the **meter (m)**.
1 meter (m) = 100 centimeters (cm),
1 centimeter (cm) = 10 millimeters (mm)
1 millimeter (mm) = 1,000 micrometers (μm)

Remember: The metric unit of volume is the **liter (L)**.
1 liter = 1000 milliliters (mL) or 1000 cubic centimeters (cm³ or cc)

Remember: The metric unit of mass is the **gram (g)**.

Remember: Mass refers to the amount of matter in an object.
1 gram = 1000 milligrams (mg)
1000 grams = 1 kilogram (kg)

Remember: The metric unit of temperature is **degree Celsius (oC)**.

CHAPTER REVIEW

1. Which one of the following statements is **true**?
   A. It is okay to enter the laboratory if your instructor is late for class.
   B. It is okay to chew gum in the laboratory.
   C. Always bring your own drinking water into the laboratory.
   D. Always wear a protective coat in the laboratory.

2. Which one of the following statements does **not** refer to a laboratory safety rule?
   A. Secure long hair, loose clothing, and jewelry for your personal safety.
   B. Keep all equipment away from the edge of your laboratory tables.
   C. Dispose of bio-hazardous waste material in the recycle bin.
   D. Wash your hands with soap and warm water before leaving the laboratory.

3. Your mouth is superior to your_____.
   A. eyes
   B. chin
   C. ears
   D. forehead

4. Which one of the following statements is **true**?
   A. The toes are distal to the knee.
   B. The big toe is proximal to the little toe.
   C. The ankle is distal to the toes.
   D. The knee is proximal to the hip.

5. Transverse planes divide the human body into _____.
   A. anterior and posterior parts
   B. superior and inferior parts
   C. left and right sides
   D. two equal parts

6. The brain shown below is divided along the _____ plane.
   A. sagittal
   B. coronal
   C. midsagittal
   D. transverse

7. The epigastric region of the abdomen is _____.
   A. just below the stomach
   B. above stomach
   C. immediately below the navel
   D. in line with the navel

8. How many millimeters are in 5m?
   A. 5 million
   B. 500
   C. 5,000
   D. 50

9. How many cubic centimeters are in 2L?
   A. 2 million
   B. 200
   C. 2,000
   D. 20

10. A centimeter is equal to _____.
    A. 0.01m
    B. 0.001m
    C. 0.1m
    D. 100m

Name: _____ Class Time: _____ Class Day: _____

Complete skill checks 1 – 3.

Skill check #1

Select the correct directional terms from the list below to complete the following sentences.

Directional Terms

Superficial   Lateral   Proximal   Deep   Medial   Distal

Use the correct directional terms to complete the sentences below.

  i)   The nose is _____ to the ears.
 ii)   The hands are _____ to the wrist.
iii)   The bones of the body are _____ to the skin.

Skill check #2

Name the planes shown in figure 1.4.

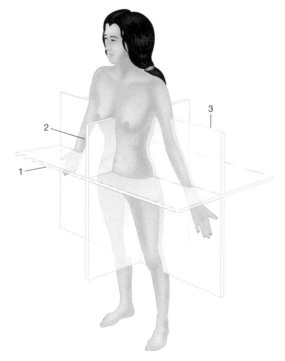

Planes:

1.   ....

2.   ....

3.   ....

Figure 1.4: Planes of body

Skill check #3

Fill in the blank spaces with appropriate values.

1. 20 mm = _____ cm

2. 150 cm = _____ m

3. Measure and record the length of the line shown below.

   _____ (_____ cm)

4. Use a measuring cylinder to measure 25 cm³ of water. Show the measuring cylinder of water to your instructor and have him or her indicate your accuracy by initiating one of the options shown below.

   Satisfactory _____   Unsatisfactory _____

5. Measure and record the mass of a Petri dish. (_____ g)

6. Measure and record the ambient (room) temperature. (_____ °C)

Note: Show these pages to your instructor once you have completed all the skill checks.

2 The Microscope

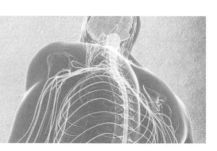

OBJECTIVES:

After completing this laboratory you should be able to perform tasks listed below.

1. Identify and state the functions of the major parts of a compound light microscope
2. Demonstrate proper use and care of the microscope.
3. Define resolution, magnification, parfocal, working distance, and depth of field.
4. Calculate total magnification.

A microscope is an instrument that allows us to observe very small objects that cannot be seen with the naked eye. Invention of the microscope made it possible for scientists to study structures of cells and the tissues. The microscope is one of the important tools that you will need to study anatomy and physiology.

A. Parts of the Compound Microscope

Head: The upper part of the microscope that contains the lenses and includes:

Ocular lenses: These are two removable lenses that you look through to observe the specimen on the slide. Some microscopes have a single ocular lens. The most common magnification of the ocular lenses is 10X, increasing the size of the specimen by a factor of 10. One of the ocular lenses may have a pointer, which is a dark line that enables the user to point to a part of the specimen on the slide.

Revolving nosepiece: This is a rotating nosepiece which carries objective lenses of different powers. The user rotates the nosepiece to change from one objective lens to another.

Objective lenses: Three to four objective lenses are usually attached to the nosepiece, with a different magnification written on each lens. The shortest of these is the scanning objective (4X) for quickly surveying the whole area of the microscope field. The mid-sized one is the low power objective (10X). The longest one is the high power objective (40X).

Arm: The vertical, usually curved or sometimes straight part connecting the head to the base of the instrument. The microscope arm contains the following parts:

Stage: The flat platform beneath the objective lenses upon which the slide is placed. The stage has either a **mechanical stage clamp** or **clips**, both of which keep the slide stationary during viewing. The **mechanical stage control (knob X-Y)** allows the precise movement of the slide on the stage.

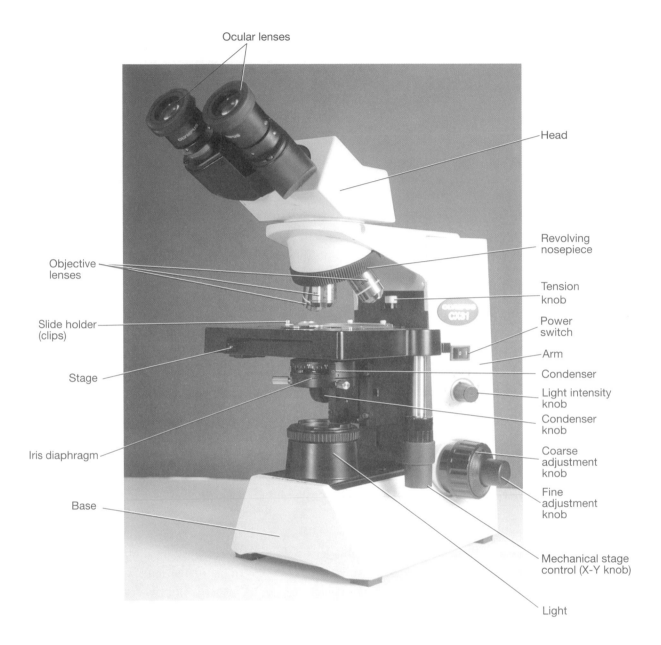

Ocular lenses

Head

Objective lenses

Revolving nosepiece

Tension knob

Power switch

Arm

Slide holder (clips)

Stage

Condenser

Light intensity knob

Condenser knob

Iris diaphragm

Coarse adjustment knob

Fine adjustment knob

Base

Mechanical stage control (X-Y knob)

Light

Figure 2.1: Parts of the compound light microscope

Coarse adjustment knobs: The larger knobs on either side of the base of the arm that allow preliminary focusing. Turning them produces relatively rapid movement of the stage bringing it closer to or further from the objective lens. **Note:** The coarse adjustment knob should only be used with the scanning power (4X) and the low power objective (10X) in order to avoid contacting the objective lens with the microscope slide.

Fine adjustment knobs: Two smaller knobs on either side of the base of the arm usually located in the center of each coarse adjustment knob. The fine adjustment knob yields extremely small movements of the stage for very precise focusing

Tension knob: Some microscopes have a tension knob that "locks in" the desired coarse focus position. This is small handle that can be found just behind the coarse adjustment knob.

Condenser: Located just below the stage, it aligns the light beam, through an opening in the stage and through the specimen. In many microscopes, the condenser includes a knob that raises and lowers the condenser to control light intensity. The best position for the condenser is close to the stage.

Condenser knob: This knob, located on the condenser, raises and lowers the condenser.

Iris diaphragm: Located under the condenser, this regulates the amount of light passing through the specimen.

Iris diaphragm lever: A lever that opens and closes a ring of metal shutters of the iris diaphragm

Base: The bottom support of the microscope. The base includes the following:

Light: A light source within the base that illuminates the specimen. Light comes from below and passes through the slide.

Power switch: A switch either at the side or front of the base turns the light on and off. A dial adjusts the light intensity.

B. Use and Care of the Microscope

Microscopes are delicate instruments that must be handled with care. Your instructor will demonstrate proper methods for transporting, cleaning, using, and storing a compound light microscope. You are expected to demonstrate these methods as you use and care your microscope.

Activity 2.1: Using the Compound Microscope

1. Find the compound microscope corresponding to your station number in the microscope cabinet under your desk. Each student should have his/her own microscope; you will **NOT** be working with a lab partner in this exercise. With one hand around the arm, the other hand supporting the base, carry the microscope to your station and place it securely on your bench.

2. Remove the dust cover from the microscope. Then, unwrap the electric cord and plug it into the electric outlet at the front of your bench.

3. Locate all the parts of your compound scope as shown in Figure 2.1.

4. Clean all lenses by applying a drop of lens cleaner and wiping with grit-free lens paper.

5. Practice focusing your scope by following the steps below:
    a. Obtain a prepared slide of the Letter "e" from the supply table. Handle a slide by the label and edges to avoid smudging it with fingerprints. Use your lens cleaner and lens paper to clean the slide.

    b. Make sure the condenser is all the way up and that the fine-focus knob is in the middle of its traveling range. If your scope has a tension knob, make sure it is unlocked.

c. Look at the slide with your naked eye and place the slide on the mechanical stage so that the "e" is right-side-up and facing forward as shown in the diagram below.

d. Center the "e" over the opening in the stage, and turn on the illuminator.

e. Look through the ocular and observe the circle of light that is called the **field of view**. Make sure the 4X scanning objective is in place over the stage opening. It will "click" in position. Then, using the coarse adjustment knob, watch the stage as you decrease the distance between slide and objective. Continue turning the coarse adjustment knob until the objective stops. On most scopes, you don't have to worry about breaking the slide with scanning and low power objectives because they will automatically stop before hitting the slide.

f. Look through the ocular, and use the coarse adjustment knob to slowly increase the distance between slide and objective until the "e" comes into focus. If your scope has a tension knob, lock in the coarse focus at the desired position. You may want to sharpen the focus using the fine adjustment knob. Adjust the diaphragm so as to reduce glare and increase contrast. If you are in the habit of using corrective glasses you may find that with proper microscope adjustment these are unnecessary. If this is uncomfortable, feel free to return to the use of your glasses. Your face should be relaxed during long periods of microscope viewing. That means no squinting. BOTH eyes are to be kept open.

g. Our compound scopes are binoculars. Look through the oculars and adjust for your interpupillary distance (distance between your eyes). Push or pull laterally on the oculars until you can view the specimen comfortably. The two eyepieces can be separately adjusted to correct for vision differences between your right and left eyes by following these steps. 1) Locate the diopter adjustment knob on the left ocular or on both oculars. Adjust it (or them) to the "zero" or middle position. 2) Close your left eye and view the specimen with your RIGHT EYE ONLY through the right ocular. Use the fine focus knob to bring the image into sharp focus. 3) Now, close your right eye and view the specimen with your LEFT EYE ONLY through the left ocular. Use the DIOPTER ADJUSTMENT to bring the image into sharp focus. 4) Open both eyes and view the specimen through both oculars. The image should now appear to be in focus with no discomfort for either eye. No additional diopter adjustment should be necessary during this session of microscope use.

h. Make sure the "e" is centered in the microscopic field. Now rotate the nosepiece until the 10X low power objective clicks into place. DO NOT adjust the stage before rotating the nosepiece. Compound microscopes are **parfocal**. That means, once you get a slide in focus under scanning power, it should also be in focus under low and high power. Therefore, you should only use the fine focus knob to sharpen the focus. If you are unable to focus the letter "e" with the fine adjustment knob, go back to step "d".

i.   Again, make sure the "e" is centered in the microscope field. Now, rotate the nosepiece until the 40X high power objective clicks into place. Remember, don't lower the stage before rotating the nosepiece - if the slide was in focus under low power, the 40X objective will clear the slide. **DO NOT USE THE COARSE ADJUSTMENT KNOB UNDER ANY CIRCUMSTANCES WITH THE 40X OBJECTIVE!** You should only need to use the fine focus knob to sharpen the image. If you are unable to focus with the fine adjustment knob, go back to step "d" or ask your instructor for help.

6.   Draw the letter "e" in the appropriate space below as it appears under the low power and high power objective of the microscope.

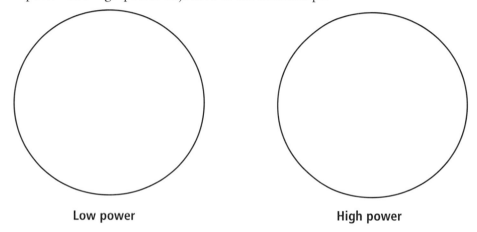

Low power   **High power**

7.   How does the image seen through the microscope compare with the image seen with the naked eye?

_____

8.   Move the slide to the right. In which direction does the image appear to move under the microscope?

_____

9.   Using the mechanical stage control, move the slide upward. In which direction does the image appear to move under the microscope?

_____

Note:
Due to inversion, if you want to move an object in one direction in the microscopic field, you must move the slide in the opposite direction on the stage.

C. Resolution and Magnification

A microscope has two distinct functions: resolution and magnification. **Resolution** is the ability of an optical system to distinguish adjacent objects as separate entities. The unaided human eye can normally distinguish objects which are no smaller than 0.1 mm. The light microscope cannot resolve objects smaller than 0.25 micrometers. The light microscope then enlarges or magnifies the resolved image to dimensions that can be perceived by the human eye. **Magnification** allows you to see an object many times larger than its actual size. The limit of useful magnification by the light microscope is about 1500X because the magnification is limited by the resolution. Magnification beyond this point would result in useless, blurred images.

Note:
Magnification is expressed in linear units, not units of area. An object magnified 4X appears twice as long and wide as one magnified 2X.

Activity 2.2: Calculating Total Magnification

When you're using the low power (10X) objective to view an object, the objective is magnifying the object ten times. But you're also looking at the object through an ocular lens (10X), which is magnifying that image ten times more. The total magnification with the low power objective is 10 x 10 or 100X.

Total magnification = objective magnification x ocular magnification.

Using this formula, complete the following table:

Power	Magnification of Objective	Magnification of Ocular	Total Magnification
Scanning		10X	
Low	10X		
High			400X

Activity 2.3: Magnification and Field of View

1. The **field of view** is the diameter of the circle of view you can see when looking through the ocular lenses on the slide.

2. Obtain a prepared slide labeled "Flea" from the supply table.

3. Using the steps in activity 2.1, focus the flea under low power.

4. While looking into the microscope, carefully move the slide so that the flea's head is just visible on the right hand side of the microscopic field as shown in the diagram below.

5. Increase magnification to high power. Is the head of the flea still in the field of view?

_____

D. Working Distance and Depth of Field

The distance between the lower end of the objective and the coverslip on the slide is called the **working distance** (Figure 2.2). The working distance decreases as magnification increases. However, the **depth of field** refers to the thickness of the specimen that may be focused on and clearly seen at one time. The depth of field also decreases with increased magnification. When viewing a specimen under high power (40X), it is necessary to use the fine focus knob to move upward or downward from one optical plane of the specimen to another, so that details will not be overlooked. In order to view the other threads, you must focus downward to view the ones underneath and upward to view the ones that are above.

Stage

Figure 2.2: Working Distance

Activity 2.4: Working Distance and Depth of Field

1. Obtain a prepared slide labeled "Colored Threads"

2. Focus the colored threads under scanning power, low power, and then high power.
    a. When using the scanning power, are you able to focus on all three colored threads at the same time? _____

    b. When using the high power objective, are you able to focus on all three colored threads at the same time? _____

Note: If you are unable to focus on all three colored threads at the same time with the high power objective, you must focus downward with the fine adjustment knob to view the ones underneath and upward to view the ones that are above.

    c. As magnification increases, does working distance increase or decrease?

    _____

    Colored threads: _____   _____   _____
                          Top   Middle   Bottom

D. Storing the Microscope

At the end of the laboratory session, you must store your scope by following the steps below:

   a. Turn off the light.
   b. Remove the slide from the stage and replace it in the slide tray.
   c. Unplug the microscope by firmly pulling the plug instead of the cord.
   d. Wrap the electric cord around the base or the back of the scope.
   e. Rotate the 4X or scanning objective into place.
   f. Use the coarse focus knob to move the stage as close to the objective as possible and lock it in this position with the tension knob if a tension knob is present.
   g. Center the mechanical stage.
   h. Place the dust cover over the microscope.
   i. Place the microscope in the numbered region of the cabinet that corresponds with your microscope number.
   j. Be sure to carry the microscope with BOTH hands. Place one hand under the base and another on the arm.

CHAPTER REVIEW

   1. When you are using a 10X ocular and the 10X objective, the image you see through the ocular is magnified _____.
       A. 40X
       B. 10X
       C. 1000X
       D. 100X

   2. The distance between the lower end of the objective and the coverslip is called the _____.
       A. field of view
       B. working distance
       C. depth of field
       D. focal length

   3. You should use the _____ to focus when you are using the 40X objective.
       A. condenser
       B. fine focus knob
       C. coarse focus knob
       D. ocular

   4. Which of the following can you use to adjust the light conditions on your specimen?
       A. Iris diaphragm
       B. Fine focus knob
       C. Coarse focus knob
       D. Objective

5. The thickness of a specimen that can be seen in focus at one time decreases as the magnification increases. This thickness is referred to as the _____.
   A. field of view
   B. working distance
   C. depth of field
   D. focal length

6. A specimen in focus at one magnification will be in focus at all magnifications, with only minor adjustments needed with the fine focus. This is because the microscope is _____.
   A. simple
   B. compound
   C. parfocal
   D. monocular

7. As you increase the magnification, the specimen you are viewing appears larger. However, you are looking at a smaller portion of the specimen. In other words, as you increase the magnification, the _____ gets smaller.
   A. field of view
   B. objective
   C. wave length
   D. ocular

8. Which of the following statements about the care of the microscope is **false**?
   A. Carry the microscope with both hands; one on the base another on the arm.
   B. Unplug the microscope by firmly pulling the plug (not the cord).
   C. Use grit-free lens paper to clean all lenses.
   D. Rotate the 40X objective into place before storing the scope.

9. If the field of view is 0.45 mm in diameter and three cells can fit lengthwise across the field of view. How long is one cell?
   A. 1.35 μm
   B. 1.35 mm
   C. 150 μm
   D. 1.5 mm

10. Which of the following statements is **false**?
    A. The most common magnification of the ocular is 10X.
    B. The coarse adjustment knob is the larger knob on either side of the microscope.
    C. The high power objective is the 10X.
    D. A microscope is an instrument that allows us to observe very small objects.

Name: _____ Class Time: _____ Class Day: _____

Complete skill checks 1 – 3.

Skill check # 1

1. What is the magnification of the ocular lenses of your microscope?

2. What is the total magnification if the ocular is 10X and the objective is 40X?

Skill check # 2

1. Draw the letter "e" in the space below as it appeared under the high power objective:

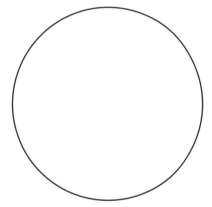

2. What happens to the field of view when you increase the magnification?

3. What happens to the detail of the specimen that you are observing when you increase the magnification and focus properly?

Skill check # 3

1. What is the distance between the tip of an objective and the slide called?

   _____

2. What happens to the distance between the objective and the stage as the magnification increases?

   _____

3 Cells and Mitosis

OBJECTIVES:

After completing this laboratory you should be able to perform tasks listed below:

1. Distinguish between the two cell types in prokaryotic and eukaryotic organisms.
2. Name and identify the major organelles found in eukaryotic cells.
3. Identify the phases of mitosis from prepared slides.
4. Explain the events of a cell's life cycle.
5. Prepare your very own onion root tip slide; you'll see how slides are made!
6. List the components of the DNA nucleotides.
7. Describe how the DNA molecule is arranged.
8. Relate the replication of DNA to the cell's life cycle

A. Two Cell Types

There are two types of cells: prokaryotic and eukaryotic. The difference is that prokaryotic cells have no defined nucleus. The prefix "pro" means before and "karyotic" means nut or kernel in Greek. The ancient anatomists thought that the nucleus looked just like a nut, like a peanut or a kernel of corn. So, eukaryotic means having a nut or kernel. If you don't have a nut or nucleus in your cell you're a prokaryote and if you do have a nut or nucleus in your cell you're a eukaryote. The best example of a prokaryotic cell is a bacterium. Plants and animals have eukaryotic cells.

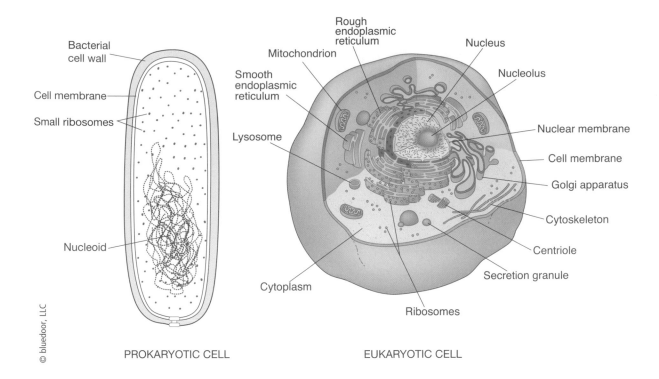

PROKARYOTIC CELL   EUKARYOTIC CELL

Figure 3.1: Prokaryote and Eukaryote

Activity 3.1: Comparing Prokaryotes and Eukaryotes

1. Examine the cells shown in Figure 3.1.

2. State the main difference between a prokaryotic and a eukaryotic cell.

_____

_____

B. Cell Structure

Cells are the basic living units of the human body. Each cell has some features that are common to other cells. A typical human cell has: 1) a **plasma membrane** 2) **cytosol**, and 3) **organelles**. The **plasma membrane** is the outermost part of the cell and it controls movement of substances into and out of the cell. **Cytosol** is a gel-like fluid that supports organelles in the cell. **Organelles** are small cellular structures with specific functions. The combination of cytosol and embedded organelles is called cytoplasm.

Nucleus: the "brain" of the cell. It contains hereditary material called DNA that directs the day to day functions of the cell. DNA and associated protein in the nucleus of a cell that is not dividing is called **chromatin**. When a cell is dividing, chromatin coils and condenses to form thread-like structures called **chromosomes**.

Nucleolus: Found inside the nucleus of the cell. It produces ribosomes.

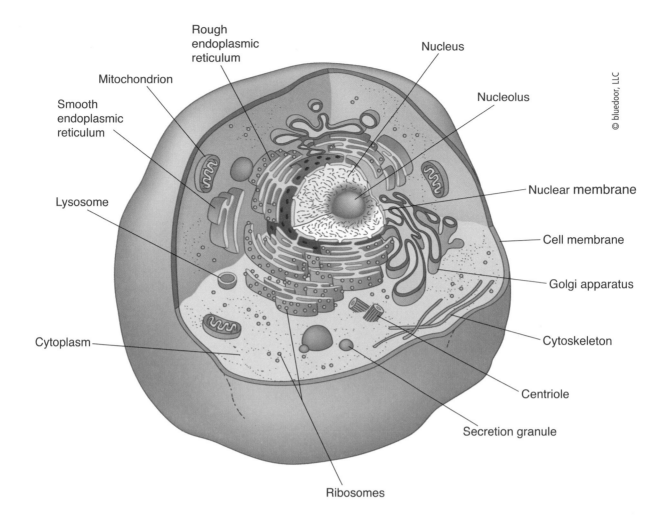

Rough
endoplasmic
reticulum

Nucleus

Mitochondrion

Nucleolus

Smooth
endoplasmic
reticulum

Nuclear membrane

Lysosome

Cell membrane

Golgi apparatus

Cytoskeleton

Cytoplasm

Centriole

Secretion granule

Ribosomes

Figure 3.2: The Animal Cell Structures

Centrioles: Organelles that form spindles for assisting the cell's division

Rough Endoplasmic Reticulum: Usually called rough ER.

Ribosomes: These are functional parts of the rough ER that assist in protein synthesis

Smooth Endoplasmic Reticulum: ER without ribosomes. It is concerned with lipid synthesis.

Golgi body: Flattened pieces of plasma membrane similar in appearance to pita breads stacked on top of each other. The Golgi body packages proteins and other substances for transport and export from the cell in **vesicles**.

Vesicles: Membrane-bound sacs that transport the cell's products.

Mitochondrion: The hot dog-shaped organelle that creates energy to power the cell.

Lysosomes (lyses = to break apart + soma = body): Lysosomes engage in intracellular digestion. Hence, they are able to clean up cellular debris.

Cilia: Short hair-like structures that extend outward, away from the cell surface and carry out rhythmic movements that propel fluids.

Activity 3.2: Studying Cell Structure

Notice that the cell in Figure 3.3 contains numbers, from 1 to 12. The numbers correspond to the name of the structures. Refer to figure 3.2 and write the appropriate name beside each number.

1 _____
2. _____
3. _____
4. _____
5. _____
6. _____
7. _____
8. _____
9. _____
10. _____
11. _____
12. _____

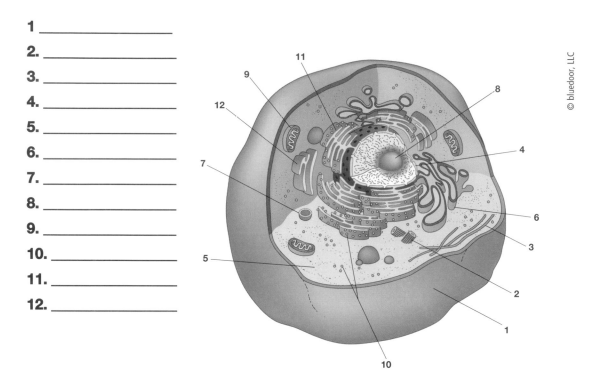

Figure 3.3: The cell drawing

C. Cell Cycle

All cells go through a life cycle called the cell cycle. There are four periods referred to as G1 period, S period, G2 period, and the M period in the life cycle of the cell. The G1 period is the first growth period of the cell. Think of a new born baby girl and all of the growth that is going on inside of her. Her organs are developing and she is growing more coordinated and stronger. The second period of the cell's cycle is called the S period for synthesis. Synthesis means to produce. In the S period of the cycle, DNA is being produced from the DNA that is already in the cell. The third period is called the G2 period because this is the growth period number two. Growth and development are completed in the G2 period and the cell prepares for division. The G1, S, and G2 periods occur between cell divisions during the phase of the cell's life called **interphase**. The fourth and final period of the cell cycle is called the M period for **Mitosis**. During this fourth period the cell shares the genetic material between two nuclei that are genetically identical.

Mitosis is nuclear division and it occurs during four phases: prophase, metaphase, anaphase and telophase. During this stage of the cell's cycle, genetic material (DNA) is divided into two equal quantities. Mitosis is followed by cytokinesis or cytoplasmic division and two new cells separate from each other during the process. **Cytokinesis** means "cell moving." The two new cells move away from each other and start their own cell cycle after cytokinesis ends.

Activity 3.3: Studying the Cell Cycle

1. Examine Figure 3.4 carefully.
2. Write the important events of a cell's life cycle in the spaces provided on Figure 3.4.

Events of a cell's life cycle:

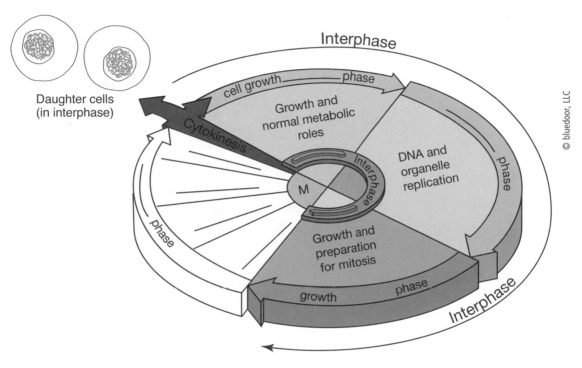

Figure 3.4: The cell cycle

Activity 3.4: Somatic Cell Division

Using models and charts that are available in your lab, study the phases of mitosis and note the changes that characterize each mitotic phase. Use Figure 3.5 to assist you.

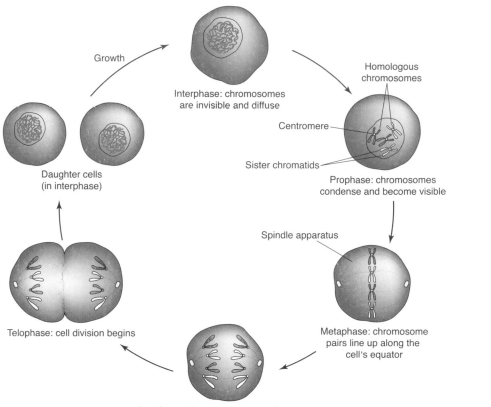

Figure 3.5: Cell Mitosis

D. Making Your Own Slide

Most of the microscope slides you will be studying in the lab will be prepared (pre-made) slides.

In this exercise, you will learn how to make your own slide!

Activity 3.5: Preparing Your Own Slide

You will be preparing an onion root tip slide by using the following procedure:

1. Clean one microscope slide
2. Using a pair of forceps, remove a single complete root from an onion bulb. Place the slide on your desk and lay the root on top of it. Keep it moist.
3. Using a magnifying glass, locate the most tapered end of the onion root tip. This is the area of mitosis.
4. With a sharp blade cut off and save the last 3 mm of the root tip. Discard the rest of the root.

5. Cover the root tip with four drops of fixative. Wait 5 minutes. Drain the liquid from the slide using a paper towel. This fixative will stop cellular activity.

6. Cover the root tip with two drops of preservative for 5 minutes. Drain the liquid from the slide using a paper towel. Keep this liquid off your skin because it can irritate your skin.

7. Cover the root tip with aceto-orcein stain for 20 minutes. **During this time go to activity 3.6 and follow the directions found there.** Make sure you keep track of the time.

8. Drain the liquid from the slide using a paper towel. Place a coverslip, a small square piece of glass onto the root tip. Apply increasing pressure straight down over the coverslip squashing the root tip.

9. Look at your slide under high power (400X). Look for a phase of mitosis (prophase, metaphase, anaphase or telophase).

To conclude the exercise, make sure all disposable items (slides, coverslips, paper towels, etc.) are properly disposed, your microscope is cleaned and put away, and your work area is wiped down.

Activity 3.6: Viewing a Prepared Slide (Do this activity while you are waiting twenty minutes for the root tip in activity 3.5 to be stained)

1. Obtain a microscope and a prepared slide of the whitefish blastula. The blastula is an early embryonic ball of actively dividing cells present during development of all multi-celled animals. It is chosen for your study because of the large size of the cells and their high level of mitotic activity.

2. Using Figure 3.6 as a reference, observe the slide under high power and identify cells that were preserved when they were undergoing interphase, prophase, metaphase, anaphase, telophase, or cytokinesis.

3. Obtain an onion root tip prepared slide and use the high power objective to observe stages of mitosis in the root tip.

4. Find the four phases of mitosis on the slides that you observe. Your instructor will check your work.

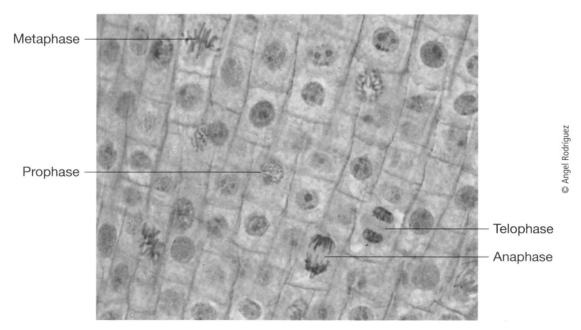

Figure 3.6: The onion root tip.

E. DNA vs. RNA

When we look inside of the nucleus we see that DNA is housed there. DNA stands for **deoxyribonucleic acid**. It's an easy concept to understand. Take the D in DNA; this is really a sugar, like table sugar. However, a molecule of this sugar has five sides, and we call it a ribose. But there is more to the story. It turns out that the sugar in DNA is lacking an oxygen atom, so it's **de** (*de* = without) **oxy** (*oxy* = oxygen). Ribose is the sugar in RNA.

Figure 3.7: The difference between deoxyribose and ribose

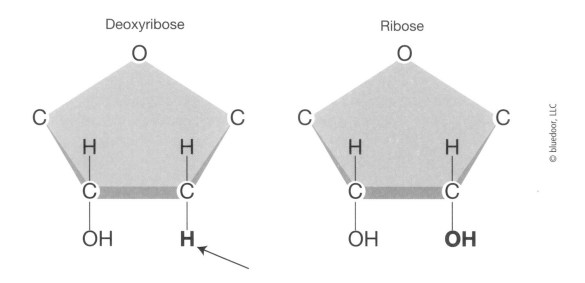

DNA STRUCTURE

While the structure of DNA is a double helix, like two spiral staircases next to each other, we can uncoil the double staircases and make a ladder. The structure of DNA can be likened to a ladder. DNA's sugar is deoxyribose which is connected to a phosphate group. This sugar and phosphate form the sides of the DNA molecule or the sides of the ladder. The steps of the ladder are bases called: Guanine (G), Cytosine (C), Adenine (A) and Thymine (T). Each step is composed of two bases that are paired or joined together.

GCAT

The bases in DNA are considered to be complimentary. G always pairs with C and A always pairs with T that spells GCAT (*"Gee CAT"*).

Figure 3.8: The structure of DNA

Phosphate

Hydrogen bonds

Deoxyribose

Guanine

Cytosine

Thymine

Adenine

DNA REPLICATION

DNA reproduces it's self in the "S" period of the cell cycle. This happens because existing DNA forms a template for making new DNA.

Activity 3.7: The DNA Model

DNA models are available in the lab. Notice the beauty and the symmetry of the DNA molecule and understand why James Watson, the co-discoverer of the structure of DNA, said "It's too beautiful not to be true!"

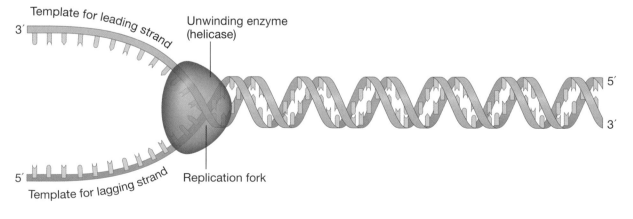

Figure 3.9: DNA replication

CHAPTER REVIEW

1. Which organelle may be shaped like a hot dog? _____

2. Which organelle contains ribosomes and serves as the site of protein synthesis?

    _____

3. Name the phases of mitosis in order: _____

4. Cytoplasm is composed of _____ and _____.

5. The organelle that appears like a stack of pita breads and packages material for
    export is the _____.

6. Which of the following organelles do you think would most likely be the "garbage
    collector" of the cell?
    A. Mitochondria
    B. Rough ER
    C. Lysosomes
    D. Golgi Body

7. How does DNA differ from RNA?

    _____

8. The phase of mitosis during which chromosomes line up along the equator of the
    cell is known as _____.

9. Name the process of cytoplasmic division of the cell into two daughter cells. It is
    the final process of somatic cell division.

    _____

10. Write the sequence of the periods in the cell cycle.

    _____

Name: _____Class Time: _____Class Day: _____

Complete skill checks 1 – 3.

Skill check #1

Know the cell structures on the cell model. Your instructor will test your knowledge by pointing at random structures.

Skill check #2

Know the phases of mitosis on the mitosis models of the animal. Study the DNA model and its components. Your instructor will ask you about these two models.

Skill check #3

Show your instructor a phase of mitosis on a prepared slide of the onion root tip or on the slide that you prepared.

4 Diffusion and Permeability

OBJECTIVES:

After completing this laboratory you should be able to perform tasks listed below.

1. Explain Brownian motion.
2. Distinguish between simple diffusion and osmosis.
3. Define solutes, solvents, and solutions.
4. Use the terms hypotonic, isotonic, and hypertonic correctly.
5. Explain crenation and hemolysis.
6. Demonstrate knowledge of principles that relate to osmotic pressure.

A. Brownian Movement

Brownian movement (named after the Scottish botanist Robert Brown) is the irregular movement of particles caused by collisions with other particles suspended in a liquid or gas. Brownian movement occurs passively. Therefore, it does not require input of energy in the form of adenosine triphosphate (ATP).

Remember: The molecules of all matter have **kinetic energy** and are in a continual state of motion.

Activity 4.1: Observing Brownian Movement

Materials
- A mixture of carmine powder and water in a dropper bottle
- 1 microscope slide and a cover slip
- Microscope

Procedure
1. Shake the bottle with carmine and water thoroughly then place a drop of the carmine mixture on the microscope slide.
2. Cover the carmine mixture with the cover slip then observe it under the low power objective of your microscope and again under the high power objective.
3. Describe and illustrate the movements of the tiny carmine particles in the spaces provided.

   a. Description of the movement of the tiny carmine particles:

   _____

   _____

b. Use arrows and dots to illustrate Brownian movement of the carmine particles in the space provided.

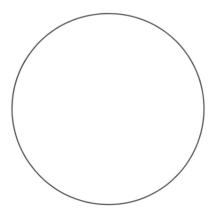

Figure 4.1: Carmine particle movements

B. Simple Diffusion

Simple diffusion is the passive net movement of molecules from an area of high concentration of a substance to an area of lower concentration of the same substance. **Passive transport** of molecules occurs down their concentration gradient. The rate of this movement can be affected by:

   i.   The steepness of the concentration gradient (difference in concentration) between the two substances.
   ii. The weight of the molecules.
   iii. The temperature of the substances.

Simple diffusion occurs if the molecules of a substance are introduced into another substance (e.g. sucrose into water). Irregular motion and collisions of molecules result in a dispersal (spreading out) of the molecules among each other.

Remember: Passive transport does not require input of energy in the form of adenosine triphosphate (ATP). The **kinetic energy** of molecules as they move and collide with each other provides energy for passive movement of substances during diffusion. Passive movement differs from **active transport** that requires input of energy in the form of adenosine triphosphate (ATP).

Activity 4.2: Observing Simple Diffusion of Dye Through Agar Gel

Pairs of students are required to complete activity 4.2.

Materials
- 1 agar gel Petri dish
- Methylene blue crystals (molecular weight = 320g)
- Potassium permanganate crystals (molecular weight = 158g)
- 2 pairs of forceps
- 1 pipette
- 1 short ruler

Procedure
1. Use the pipette to create two tiny wells 5 cm apart in the agar gel of the Petri dish.
2. Use one pair of forceps to carefully place a methylene blue crystal into one well in the agar gel.
3. Note and record the time.
4. Use the other pair of forceps to carefully place a potassium permanganate crystal into the other well in the agar gel. See Figure 4.2.
5. Leave the Petri dish on your lab bench and measure the diameter of the space occupied by each dye the first 5 minutes then after 30 minutes.
6. Based on difference in molecular weight, predict which dye will move faster.
7. Prediction: _____
8. Record your results (data) in Table 4.1.
9. Calculate the diffusion rate of each dye and write a summary of your results.

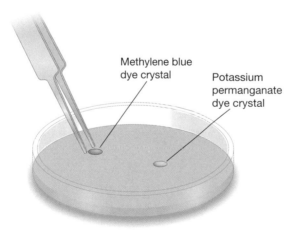

Methylene blue
dye crystal

Potassium
permanganate
dye crystal

© bluedoor, LLC

Figure 4.2: Agar gel Petri dish setup

Table 4.1: Diameter of space occupied by methylene blue and potassium permanganate

Time (Min)	Diffusion diameter: Methylene blue (mm)	Diffusion diameter: potassium permanganate (mm)
5		
30		

Summary of results: _____

_____

_____

C. Osmosis

Osmosis is a special kind of diffusion. During osmosis, there is passive net movement of solvent (water) molecules across a selectively permeable membrane (such as a cell membrane) from a region of its high concentration to a region of its lower concentration. A **hypotonic solution** has a lower concentration of solutes than the concentration of solutes in a **hypertonic solution**. If two solutions of different solute concentration (tonicity) are separated by a selectively permeable membrane, osmosis will occur until equilibrium is attained and both solutions contain equal concentrations of solutes. **Isotonic solutions** have equal solute concentrations.

Note:
- If a red blood cell is placed in a hypertonic solution, it will lose most of its water and become **crenated**. **Crenation** is the process by which a cell loses water and so will become shriveled, the cell with have a spiked appearance as a result of crenation.

- If a red blood cell is placed in a hypotonic solution, it will gain water by osmosis, become swollen, and then burst. **Hemolysis** (Hemo = blood; lysis = breakdown) is the process by which red blood cells burst because of intake of excess water.

Note: Water in a cell presses against the cell membrane and exerts an **osmotic pressure.**

Note:
A **solvent**, such as water, dissolves a solute.
A **solute,** such as sucrose, is the substance dissolved in a solvent.
A **solution** is formed when a solute is dissolved in a solvent.
The solute concentration of a solution is described as the **tonicity.**

Remember: A selectively permeable membrane only allows small molecules to pass through.

Activity 4.3: Detecting Simple Diffusion and Osmosis Through a Nonliving Membrane

Students are required to work in groups of 4 on activity 4.3.

Materials

- A 14-cm length of dialysis tubing soaked in water
- clip
- distilled water
- 1% starch solution
- 80% glucose solution
- 10% sodium chloride solution
- A dropper bottle containing Lugol's reagent (iodine solution)
- A dropper bottle containing silver nitrate solution
- A dropper bottle containing Benedict's solution
- A 400-mL beaker
- A 10-mL graduated cylinders
- A glass rod (stirrer)
- 3 test tubes
- A boiling water bath
- An electronic balance

Procedure

1. Place 200mL distilled water into the 400-mL beaker.
2. Add 20 drops of Lugol's reagent to the water in the beaker and stir with the glass rod.
   Remember: Lugol's reagent causes starch to appear blue-black.
3. Obtain a piece of soaked dialysis tubing from the supply area.
   Fold over one end of the tubing and seal with a clip.
4. Measure 25 mL of 1% starch solution and pour it into the tied dialysis tubing   (bag).
5. Add 30 drops of 80% glucose solution and 30 drops of 10% sodium chloride solution to the starch solution in the dialysis bag.
6. Carefully squeeze the top section of the bag to expel excess air.
7. Fold over and seal the top of the dialysis bag with a clip.
8. Rinse the bag with distilled water and gently pat it dry with a paper towel.
9. Use the electronic balance to weigh the dry bag.
10. Record the initial mass of the bag in the space provided. Then carefully submerge it into the beaker of distilled water and iodine solution. See figure 4.
    Note: The solution in the beaker should remain golden brown for a few minutes after the dialysis bag has been submerged into it.
11. Leave the setup for 30 minutes.
12. After 30 minutes remove the bag from the beaker, pat it dry, and reweigh it.
13. Record the final mass and the appearance of the bag in the space provided.
14. Pour another 1 mL sample of the beaker solution **into another clean test tube** and perform a reducing sugar test by heating the solution with 1mL of Benedict's solution in a boiling water bath. A change in the color of Benedict's solution indicates presence of reducing sugars. Record your observation in Table 4.2.
15. Pour a 1 mL sample of the beaker solution into a clean test tube and add a drop of silver nitrate solution. The appearance of a white precipitate or cloudiness indicates a reaction of silver nitrate with sodium chloride. Record your observation in Table 4.2.
16. Write a summary of your results in the space provided.

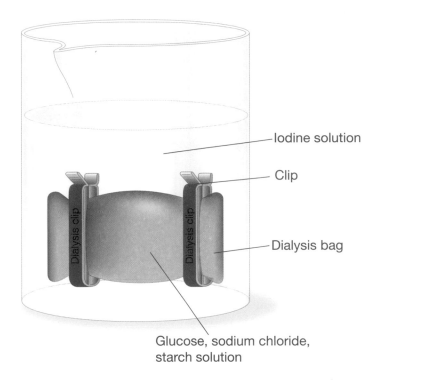

Figure 4.3: Dialysis bag and iodine solution setup

Results

Initial mass of the bag =

Final mass of the bag =

% Change in mass of the bag =

Appearance of bag after 30 minutes: _____

Table 4.2: Observations and explanations

Test of beaker solution after 30 minutes	Observations	Explanations
1. Silver nitrate test		
2. Benedict's test		

Summary of results:_____

_____

Activity 4.4: Detecting Osmosis Through a Living Cell Membrane
Students are required to work in groups of 4 on activity 4.4.

Materials
- Sheep's blood
- A disposable pipette for blood
- 3 microscope slides and 3 cover slips
- Distilled water in a dropper bottle
- Physiological saline [0.9% sodium chloride (NaCl) solution] in a dropper bottle.
  Note: Physiological saline is isotonic to blood.
- 10% sodium chloride solution in a dropper bottle
- A wax pencil

Procedure
1. Label each slide appropriately for you to distinguish distilled water, 0.9% sodium chloride solution, and 10% sodium chloride solution.
2. Place a drop of 0.9% sodium chloride solution in the depression on the slide labeled 0.9% sodium chloride. Then add 1 drop of sheep's blood.
3. Place a cover slip over the blood and observe the shape of red blood cells under the low and high power objectives of the microscope.
   Note: A red blood cell is a very tiny concave, disc-shaped structure that lacks a nucleus.
4. Use the terms **crenation** and **hemolysis** to help you describe and explain the appearance of the red blood cells in Table 4.3.
5. Illustrate the appearance of the cells in the appropriate circles of Figure 4.4.
6. Repeat steps 2-4 using distilled water and then 10% sodium chloride solution.
7. Dispose of slides as directed by your instructor.

Table 4.3: Appearance of red blood cells and explanations

Treatment of blood cells	Appearance	Explanations
Placed in physiological saline		
Placed in distilled water		
Placed in 10% sodium chloride solution		

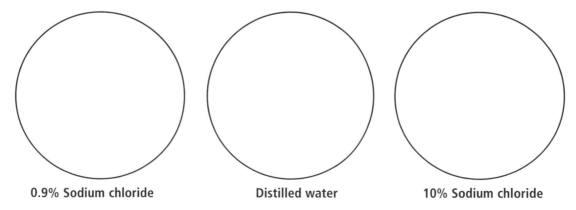

| 0.9% Sodium chloride | Distilled water | 10% Sodium chloride |

Figure 4.4: Illustration of red blood cells

CHAPTER REVIEW

1. Water molecules move passively across a cell membrane by _____.
   A. osmosis
   B. facilitated diffusion
   C. simple diffusion
   D. active transport

2. Which one of the following processes occurs when sodium ions move up their concentration gradient?
   A. Osmosis
   B. Active transport
   C. Simple diffusion
   D. Facilitated diffusion

3. Adenosine triphosphate (ATP) is utilized during _____.
   A. active transport
   B. facilitated diffusion
   C. simple diffusion
   D. osmosis

4. Cell (plasma) membranes are _____.
   A. fully permeable
   B. impermeable to all solutes
   C. impermeable to 50% of any solute in a solution
   D. selectively permeable

5. Solution A is hypertonic to a solution B. Therefore, solution A has_____.
   A. much more solvent than solution B
   B. exactly the same solute content as solution B
   C. proportionately more solute than solution B
   D. proportionately less solute than solution B

6. Red blood cells were unaffected by being submerged in sodium chloride solution in a test tube. Which one of the following terms correctly describes the tonicity of the solution?
   A. Hypotonic
   B. Hypertonic
   C. Isotonic
   D. Neutral

7. Two selectively permeable sacs A and B were submerged in a 45% glucose solution that was contained in a beaker. Sac A contained a 15% glucose solution and Sac B contained a 15% sucrose solution. In which direction did net movement of water molecules occur?
   A. Only from Sac A to the beaker
   B. Only from Sac B to the beaker
   C. From the beaker to both sacs
   D. From both sacs to the beaker

8. Which one of the following terms refers to irregular movement of charcoal dust in water?
    A. Simple diffusion
    B. Osmosis
    C. Brownian movement
    D. Active transport

9. Red blood cells that were covered with distilled water on a microscope slide became swollen and eventually ruptured. Which one of the following terms refers specifically to rupturing of blood cells?
    A. Crenation
    B. Hemolysis
    C. Hydrolysis
    D. Lysis

10. Red blood cells became shrunken after being flooded with sodium chloride solution on a microscope slide. Which one of the following terms refers specifically to shrinkage of blood cells?
    A. Crenation
    B. Dehydration
    C. Shriveling
    D. Water loss

Name: _____ Class Time: _____ Class Day: _____

Complete skill checks 1 – 3.

Skill check #1

Name and describe the type of particle movement shown in Figure 4.5.

_____

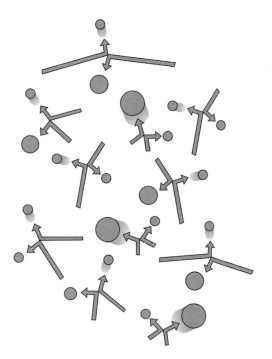

Figure 4.5: Particle movement

Skill check #2

Which of the following two dyes diffused at a faster rate? Circle your answer and state a reason for the difference in diffusion rates of the dyes.

A. Methylene blue   B. Potassium permanganate

Reason_____

Skill check #3

Based on your observations of the red blood cells, which one of the following two solutions was hypertonic? Circle your answer and state the reason for your answer.

A. 0.9% Sodium chloride   B. 10% Sodium chloride

Reason_____

5 Tissues

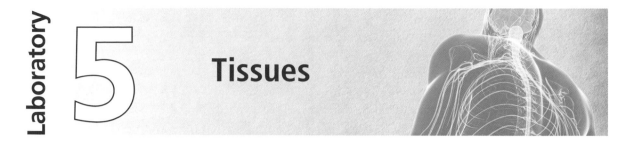

OBJECTIVES:

After completing this laboratory you should be able to perform tasks listed below.

1. Name the categories of tissues.
2. Describe the properties distinguishing the four basic types of tissues.
3. State the location and functions of various tissue types.
4. Identify, from prepared slides, selected types of epithelial, connective, muscle and nervous tissue.
5. Identify the structures of epidermal and dermal layers of skin.
6. Identify the major parts of the epidermal derivatives, nails and hair.

TISSUES

A tissue is a combination of similar cells that are grouped together to perform a particular function. Different tissues provide different functions such as protection, secretion, contraction or transmission of nerve impulses. The human body consists of four basic tissue types: epithelial, connective, muscle, and nervous. We use a microscope to observe and study the different types of tissues.

A. Epithelial Tissue

Epithelial tissue or epithelium is distinguished from other tissues because the cells are packed closely together. Little or no intercellular material exists between epithelial cells. Also, epithelium is avascular (*a* = without + *vasculum* = small vessel) because these cells do not allow blood vessels to pass between them. Structurally, epithelial tissue consists of an apical or free end and a basal surface attached to connective tissue. There is a basement membrane that consists of a thin layer of protein fibers beneath the basal surface. It connects the epithelial tissue to the underlying connective tissue. The function of epithelium is to cover the surface of other tissues, form the lining of body cavities, and form glands.

There are several types of epithelial tissues in the body that are classified according to the shape of the apical cells and the number of layers that the tissue forms. If the tissue consists of a single layer of cells, it is called simple epithelium. If it consists of two or more layers, it is called stratified epithelium. The functions provided by simple epithelium include diffusion, secretion, absorption, and filtration. The stratified epithelium creates a thicker layer that provides protection. Glandular epithelium secretes various products. These glands are divided into two major categories: exocrine and endocrine glands. Exocrine glands secrete products into body cavities and surfaces by way of tubular ducts. However, endocrine glands secrete their products into the blood which transports them throughout the body. The secretions of endocrine glands are called hormones.

The four categories of epithelial cells are **squamous** (*squama* = scale), which have flat cells with a disc-shape central nucleus; **cuboidal**, or cube-shaped with a round central nucleus; **columnar**, or rectangular with an spherical central nucleus toward the basal portion of each cell; and **transitional**, which resembles stratified cuboidal cells when the tissue is relaxed and resemble squamous cells when the tissue is distended or stretched.

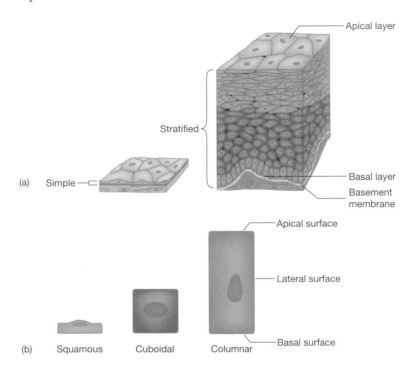

Figure 5.1: Classification of epithelial tissue

Activity 5.1: Studying Epithelium

Before proceeding, review the proper handling and care of the microscope (Laboratory 2). Remember to follow the same procedures every time you use the microscope.

1. Observe the major types of epithelial tissue listed below with the scanning, low, and high power objectives of your microscope. Be sure to recognize the characteristics of the apical or free surface and the basal membrane of the following tissues on the prepared slides.

    Simple squamous epithelium – lung slide
    Stratified squamous epithelium – all skin slides
    Simple cuboidal epithelium – kidney slide
    Simple columnar epithelium with goblet cells – colon slide
    Pseudostratified columnar epithelium – trachea slide
    Transitional epithelium – urinary bladder slide

2. Let your instructor know when you feel you can recognize the different types of epithelial tissue. Your instructor will choose one of the tissues for you to identify under the microscope.

3. Answer the questions at the end of the study section.

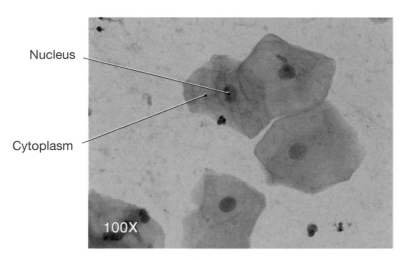

Figure 5.2: Simple Squamous Epithelium

Description: The simple squamous epithelium is composed of a single layer of flat scale-like cells.
Location: Found in the glomeruli of the kidney, the serosa, the lining of blood vessels, the heart and lymphatic vessels.
Function: The main functions of this tissue are filtration, diffusion, osmosis, and secretion.

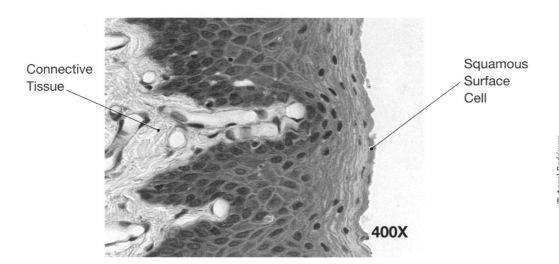

Figure 5.3: Stratified Squamous Epithelium

Description: The stratified squamous epithelium consists of several layers of flat scale-like cells.
Location: Keratinized type forms the epidermis of the skin. Non-keratinized type lines the esophagus, mouth, and vagina.
Function: The main function of this tissue is to provide protection to underlying structures.

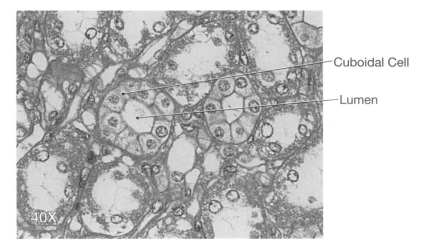

Cuboidal Cell

Lumen

40X

Figure 5.4: Simple Cuboidal Epithelium

Description: The simple cuboidal epithelium is a single layer of cube-shaped cells that line the ducts of numerous glands.
Location: Found in the tubules of the kidney, the surface of the ovaries, and secretory portions of small glands.
Function: Primarily functions in secretion and absorption

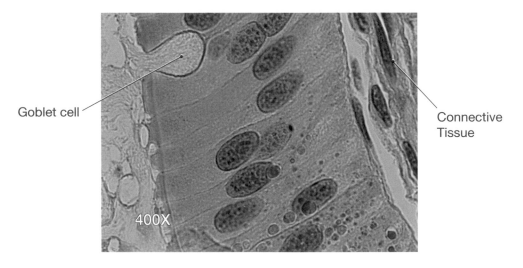

Goblet cell

Connective Tissue

400X

Figure 5.5: Simple Columnar Epithelium

Description: Simple columnar epithelium is a single layer of rectangular cells associated with goblet cells.
Location: The non-ciliated type lines the stomach and the intestinal tract. The ciliated type lines the uterine tube, parts of the uterus, and small bronchi.
Function: The main function of the ciliated type is to transport particles or fluids along a passageway.

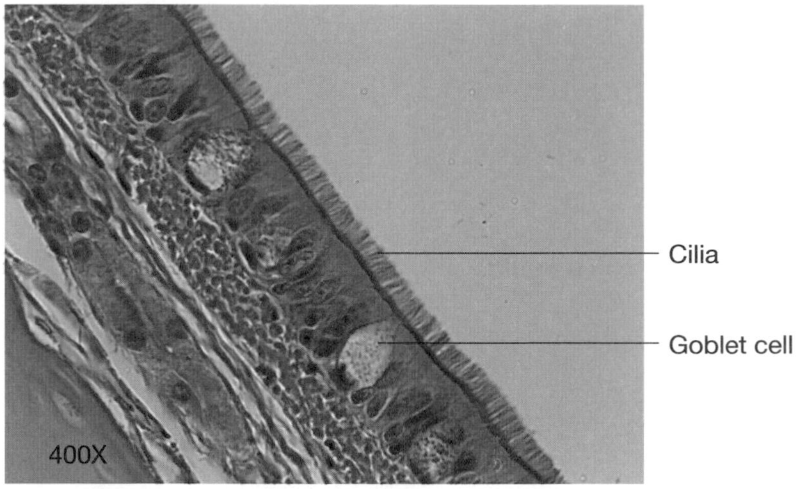

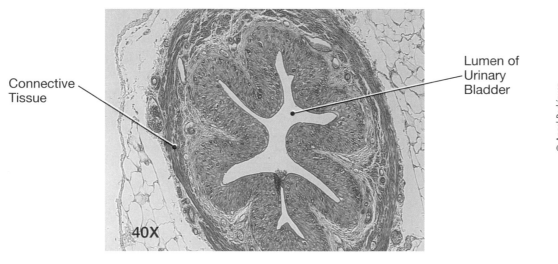

Figure 5.6: Pseudostratified Columnar Epithelium

Description: One layer of cells giving the impression of several layers. The cells are of different heights with nuclei at different levels. Goblet cells and cilia are present.

Location: Ciliated type lines the trachea and the upper respiratory tract. Non-ciliated type lines large glands and portions of the male urethra.

Function: The main functions of this tissue are secretion of mucus and movement of mucus by ciliary action.

Figure 5.7: Transitional Epithelium

Description: The transitional epithelium varies in shape from scale-like to cuboidal according to the degree of stretching.

Location: Lines the ureters, the urinary bladder, and portions of the urethra.

Function: The primary function is to allow stretching of the urinary bladder, ureters, and urethra.

Answer the following questions after studying and observing the epithelial tissues under the microscope.

1. Why does simple squamous epithelium line structures such as blood vessels?

2. Simple columnar epithelium exists as ciliated and non-ciliated forms. Contrast and compare these tissues.

_____

_____

3. What is the primary function of stratified epithelium? _____

4. What is the function of goblet cells? _____

5. What function is provided by keratin? _____

B. Connective Tissue

Connective tissue is found in all parts of the body and it arises from an early embryonic connective tissue called mesenchyme. Connective tissue is the most abundant tissue found in the human body. As the name indicates, one of the functions of connective tissue is to bind and support other tissues in the body. Additionally, connective tissue provides protection.

The living cells are surrounded by a nonliving extracellular material containing a **matrix** of **ground substance** and **fibers**. The cells produce the protein fibers which are found in the matrix. Collagen fibers, elastic fibers, and reticular fibers are types of protein fibers produced by the cells. The ground substance varies in consistency from fluid in the case of plasma in blood, gelatinous, to solid. Ground substances function as a medium for support, strength and diffusion in connective tissues. The density, distribution and arrangement of protein fibers and ground substance vary from one connective tissue type to another.

Activity 5.2: Studying Connective Tissue

1. Observe the major types of connective tissue listed below with the scanning, low, and high power objectives of your microscope. Be sure to recognize the characteristics of connective tissue on the prepared slides.

    Mesenchyme – mesenchymal cells and ground substance
    Areolar connective tissue – fibroblast, collagen, & elastic fibers
    Adipose connective tissue – fat cells & fat vacuoles
    Reticular connective tissue – reticular cells & fibers
    Dense regular connective tissue – collagen fibers & fibroblasts
    Dense irregular connective tissue - collagen fibers & fibroblasts in the dermis
    Hyaline Cartilage – chondrocytes in lacunae & matrix
    Elastic Cartilage – chondrocytes in lacunae, elastic fibers & matrix
    Compact bone – Osteons (Harvesian systems)
    Blood- Red, white blood cells and platelets with a fluid matrix

2. Let your instructor know when you feel you can recognize the different types of connective tissue. Your instructor will choose one of the tissues for you to identify under the microscope.

3. Answer the questions at the end of the study section.

Mesenchymal
Cells

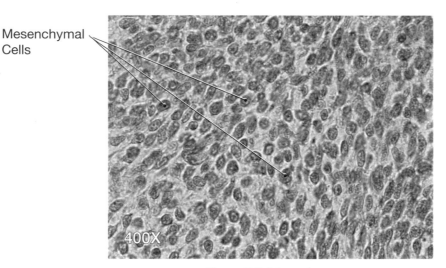

© Angel Rodriguez

Figure 5.8: Mesenchyme

Description: The mesenchyme is embryonic connective tissue. Gel like substance containing protein
    fibers.
Location: Embryonic stages
Function: Gives rise to all other types of connective tissues.

Collagen
Fibers

Elastic Fiber

Fibroblast

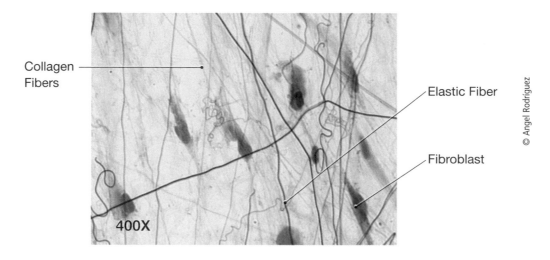

© Angel Rodriguez

Figure 5.9: Areolar Connective Tissue

Description: The areolar connective tissue contains loosely organized elastic, collagen, and reticular fibers as
    well as cells such as macrophages and fibroblasts surrounded by a semifluid ground substance.
Location: Surrounds capillaries and internal organs. Commonly found under epithelial tissue and in skin.
Function: The fibers within the tissue provide elasticity, strength, and support to connecting tissues and
    organs.

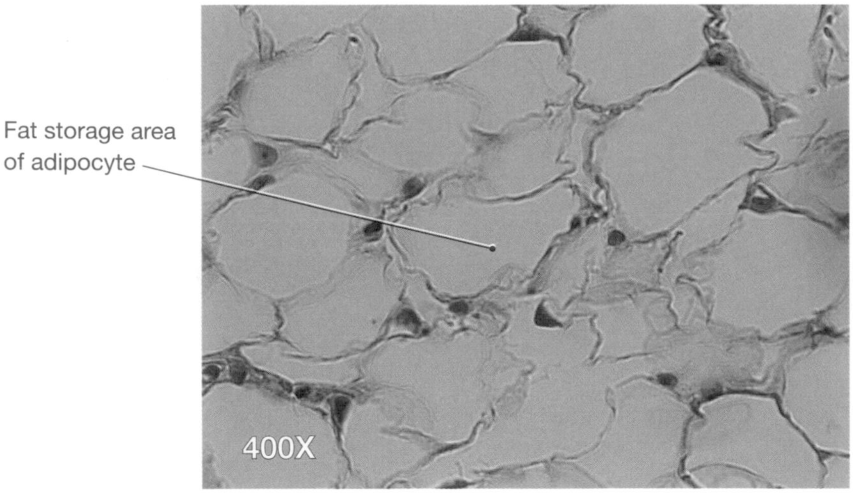

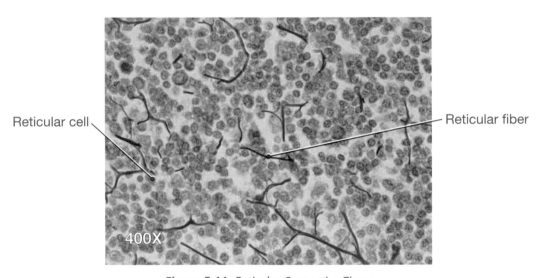

Fat storage area
of adipocyte

400X

© Angel Rodriguez

Figure 5.10: Adipose Tissue

Description: The adipose tissue is composed of adipocytes with large quantities of fat and oil.
Location: Surrounding internal organs, under the skin, in long bones, in the breast, and in the abdominal area.
Function: The main functions of this tissue are to store fat for insulation, energy, protection and support other tissues and internal organs.

Reticular cell

Reticular fiber

400X

© Angel Rodriguez

Figure 5.11: Reticular Connective Tissue

Description: The reticular connective tissue has reticular cells and a network of interwoven reticular fibers.
Location: In the lymph nodes, spleen, and bone marrow.
Function: The main functions of this tissue are to form the framework or matrix of an organ.

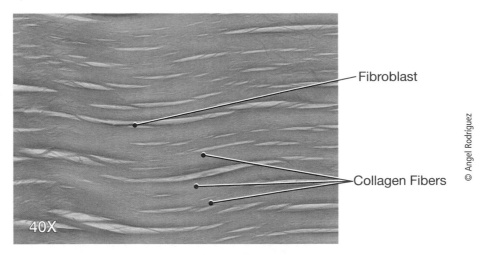

Figure 5.12: Dense Regular Connective Tissue

Description: The dense regular connective tissue consists of fibroblasts and collagen fibers arranged parallel to each other.

Location: Sheet-like fibrous membranes (aponeuroses), tendons, and most ligaments.

Function: It serves as a strong attachment between muscles and bones (tendons), and bones and bones (ligaments).

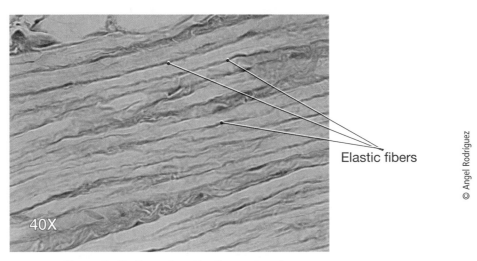

Figure 5.13: Dense Irregular Connective Tissue

Description: The dense irregular connective tissue consists of fibroblasts along with irregularly arranged collagen and elastic fibers.

Location: The fibrous capsule of joints, the dermis, and the submucosa of the gastrointestinal tract.

Function: The main function of this tissue is to provide strength. It withstands tension from many directions.

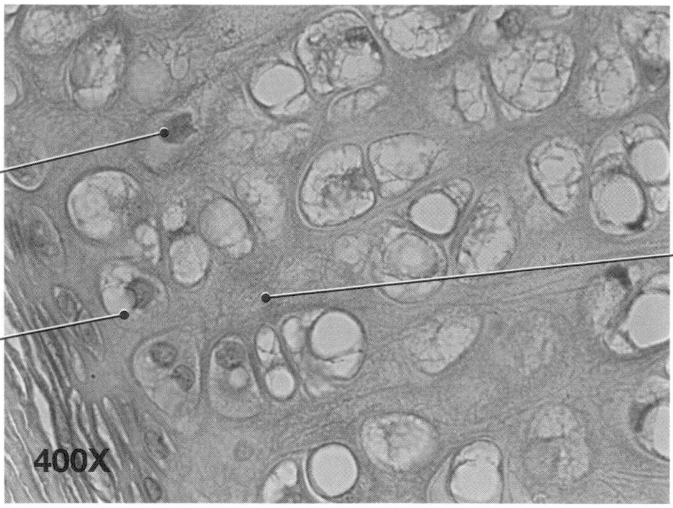

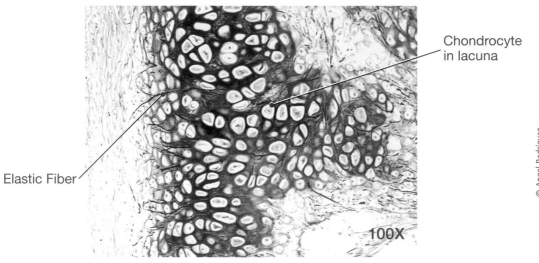

© Angel Rodriguez

Figure 5.14: Hyaline Cartilage

Description: The hyaline cartilage, is composed of chondrocytes in a matrix that contains fine collagen fibers. Chondrocytes resemble eyeballs.

Location: Found in most of the embryonic skeleton; covers the end of long bones and joints; forms the nose, trachea, larynx, and cartilage of the ribs.

Function: Hyaline cartilage forms smooth surfaces on bones enabling movement of joints and providing flexibility and support.

© Angel Rodriguez

Figure 5.15: Elastic Cartilage

Description: Elastic cartilage is composed of chondrocytes in a matrix that contains numerous thread- like elastic fibers.

Location: Forms the external ear and the epiglottis.

Function: Elastic cartilage supports and maintains the shape of the epiglottis, external ear, and the auditory canal.

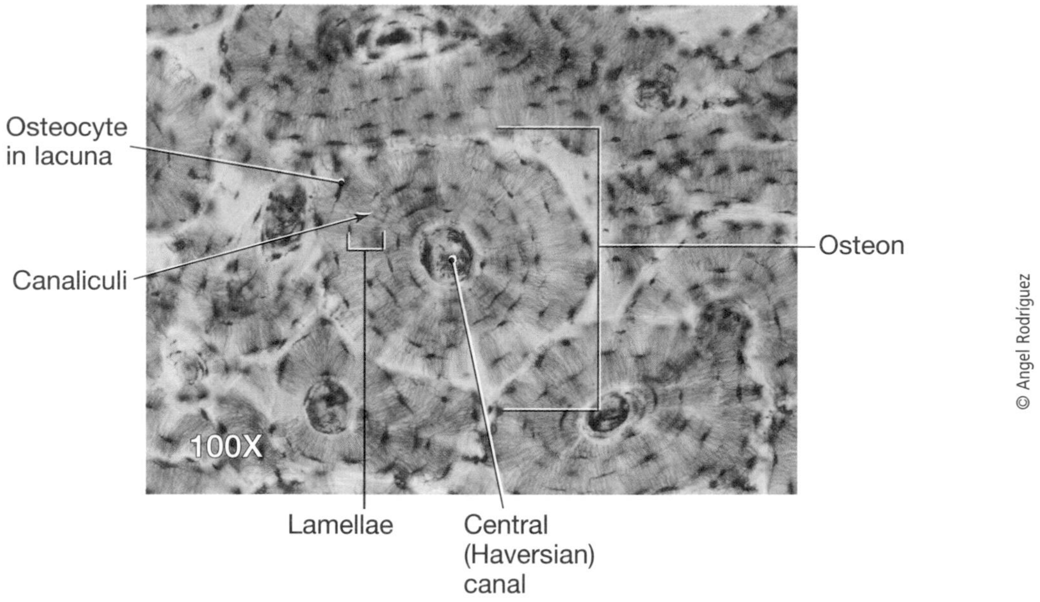

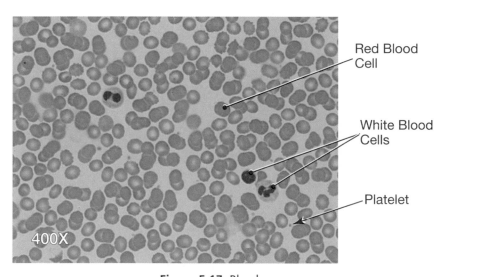

Figure 5.16: Compact Bone

Description: Compact bone contains osteocytes that are embedded in lacunae of osteons.
Location: Bones
Function: The main functions of this tissue are stores ions and minerals, supports the body, and protects surrounding tissues and organs, and works with the muscular system to provide movement.

Figure 5.17: Blood

Description: Red blood cells, white blood cells, and platelets (formed elements) suspended in a fluid matrix (plasma).
Location: In the blood vessels and heart.
Function: Red blood cells transport oxygen and carbon dioxide . White blood cells participate in allergic and immune responses. Platelets are involved with blood clotting.

C. Muscle Tissue

Muscle tissue is a specialized tissue for contraction. The cells contain molecular filaments of the proteins myosin and actin. Protein fibers of muscle are arranged in parallel bundles called fascicles. The contraction of many muscle cell fibers in a coordinated fashion causes the movement of structures in the body. During muscle contraction, the body produces heat. Hence, muscle tissue also contributes to the homeostasis of the body by regulating the internal temperature.

Muscle tissue can be classified into three types: skeletal, smooth and cardiac muscle. Skeletal muscle tissue is the primary tissue of the muscular system, which is attached primarily to bones.

Smooth muscle tissue is non-striated and has fusiform (spindle-shaped) cells with a single central nucleus per cell. This tissue forms sheets that contract the walls of hollow organs such as the stomach, the small intestine, and blood vessels. The involuntary contractions of the smooth muscle cause peristalsis which moves food through the digestive system.

Skeletal muscle cells or fibers are long and cylindrical in shape, multi nucleated, and run parallel to each other. The arrangement of the contractile units called sarcomeres produces a striped appearance or striations characteristic of skeletal muscle. Skeletal muscle contraction is controlled consciously. Therefore, it is considered to be voluntary.

Cardiac muscle has branched cells that contain striations, and usually one central nucleus per cell. Because all the fibers contract all at once, there is a gap junction between adjacent cells called intercalated discs. This involuntary muscle forms the walls of the heart and is responsible for the circulation of blood throughout the body.

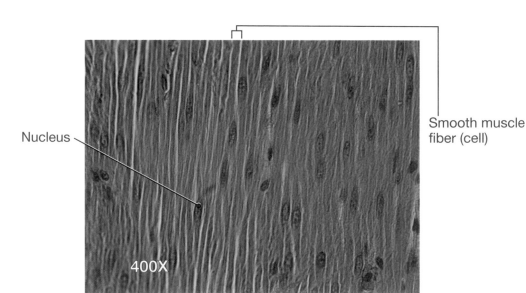

Nucleus

Smooth muscle fiber (cell)

400X

© Angel Rodriguez

Figure 5.18: Smooth Muscle

Description: Smooth muscle is composed of fusiform, non-striated muscle fibers. Each fiber contains a centrally located nucleus.
Location: The wall of hollow organs
Function: The main function of this tissue is to aid in the constriction of internal organs, blood vessels, and the gastrointestinal tract.

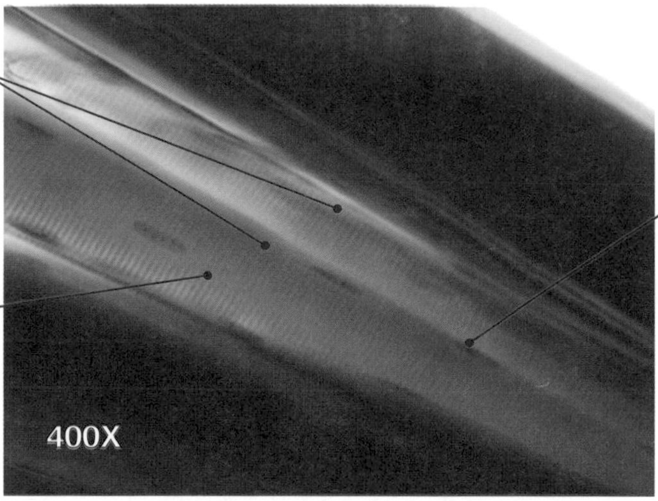

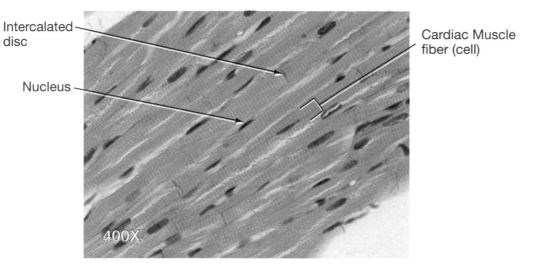

Figure 5.19: Skeletal Muscle

Description: The skeletal muscle consists of striated, multi-nucleated, unbranched muscle fibers.
Location: Skeletal muscles
Function: The skeletal muscle, in conjunction with the skeletal system, functions in heat production, motion, and posture.

Figure 5.20: Cardiac Muscle

Description: Cardiac muscle contains branched, striated fibers with one or two centrally located nuclei. The fibers are separated by intercalated discs.
Location: The heart walls
Function: Forms the heart wall and facilitates pumping of blood.

Activity 5.3: Studying Muscle Tissue

1. Observe the different types of muscle tissue listed below with the scanning, low, and high power objectives of your microscope. Be sure to recognize the general characteristics of each muscle tissue such as the location of the nuclei, and shape of the muscle fibers on the prepared slides.

    Smooth muscle

    Skeletal muscle

    Cardiac muscle

2. Let your instructor know when you feel you can recognize the different types of muscle tissue. Your instructor will choose one of the tissues for you to identify under the microscope.

3. Answer the questions at the end of the study section.

1. What is the function of the fibers in skeletal muscle tissue?

    _____

2. What is the function of smooth muscle tissue?

    _____

3. What structure does cardiac muscle tissue form? _____

4. Contrast skeletal muscle tissue and smooth muscle tissue.

    _____

    _____

D. Nervous Tissue

Nervous tissue is highly specialized to conduct nerve impulses. The cells forming the nervous tissue are called neurons and neuroglia. These cells are found in the brain, spinal cord, and nerves. Neurons have different shapes. The most common one, the multipolar neuron, contains a long process called an axon and a cell body (soma) with several smaller processes called dendrites. The axon conducts electrical signals to other cells and the dendrites receive signals from other cells. Neuroglia support and protect neurons.

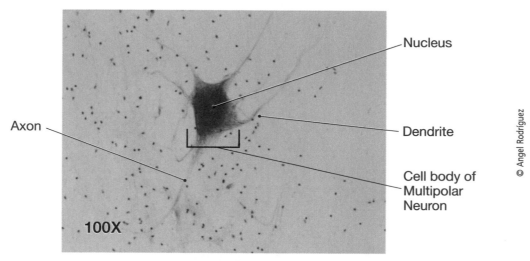

Figure 5.21: Multipolar Neuron

Description: Nervous tissue is composed of neurons and surrounding neuroglia.
Location: The nerves, the spinal cord, and the brain.
Function: The main functions of this tissue are to receive and transmit nerve impulses.

Activity 5.4: Studying Nervous Tissue

1. Observe the nervous tissue with the scanning, low, and high power objectives of your microscope. Be sure to recognize the general characteristics of the multipolar neuron,on the prepared slide.

2. Let your instructor know when you feel you can recognize the general characteristics of the nervous tissue. Your instructor will choose parts of the multipolar neuron for you to identify under the microscope.

E. The Skin

The skin has two regions: the **epidermis** (epi- = on top + dermis = skin and the **dermis**. The epidermis is superficial it is composed primarily of stratified squamous epithelim. Hairs, hair follicles, and nails are epidermal derivatives. The dermis is deep and it composed primarily of connective tissues that support accessory structures such as hair, hair follicles, sebaceous glands, sweat glands, nerves, and blood vessels. The dermis consists of two regions: the **papillary region** and the **reticular region** (Figure 5.22).

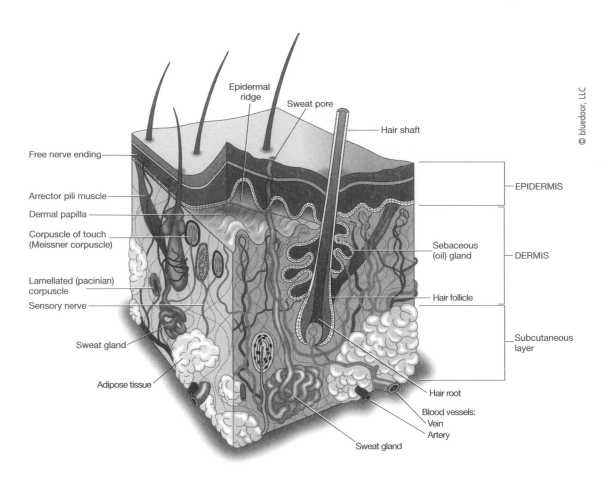

Figure 5.22: Human Skin

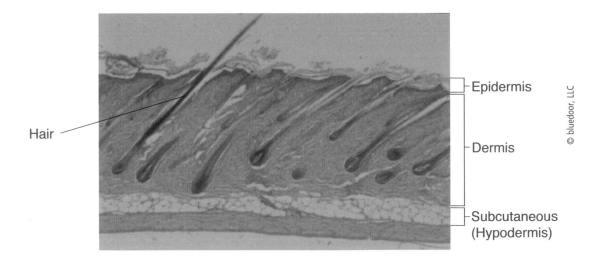

Figure 5.23: Photomicrograph of human skin

Activity 5.5: Studying the Anatomy of the Skin

1. Examine a model of the skin and note the location of the regions and accessory structures.
2. Refer to figure 5.22. Then, identify the regions and accessory structures of the skin model.
3. Carefully observe a prepared slide of the human hairy skin with the scanning, low, and high power objectives of your microscope.
4. Refer to figure 5.23 and identify the regions as well as the visible accessory structures of the skin.
5. Let your instructor know when you feel you can recognize the regions of the skin and the accessory structures. Your instructor will choose one of the structures for you to identify under the microscope or on a model of the skin.

F. The Nails

Nails are located at the distal ends of digits. The nails are primarily concerned with protecting the digits. However, they also help us to grip and manipulate objects. Each nail is composed of a free edge, body, and root (Figure 5.24).

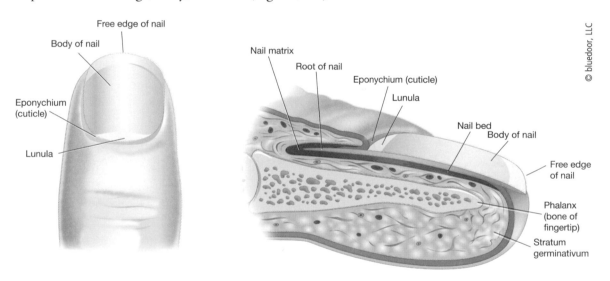

© bluedoor, LLC

Figure 5.24: Structure of human nail

Activity 5.6: Identifying Parts of a Nail

1. Study figure 5.24 and note the location of the parts of a human nail.
2. Examine your finger nails and identify the parts listed below.

   Free edge
   Body of nail
   Lunula
   Eponychium (cuticle)

3. Let your instructor know when you feel you can recognize the visible parts of your nails. Your instructor will choose one of the structures for you to identify.

CHAPTER REVIEW

1. Which of the following statements is **false**?
    A. Epithelial tissue or epithelium supports and binds other organs.
    B. Connective tissue binds and supports other tissues in the body.
    C. Skeletal muscle causes the movement of structures in the body.
    D. Nervous tissue is highly specialized to react to stimuli and to conduct nerve impulses.

2. Which type of tissue is specialized for contraction?
    A. skeletal muscle
    B. smooth muscle
    C. cardiac muscle
    D. all of the above

3. Which type of tissue supports and binds other tissues?
    A. epithelial
    B. connective
    C. muscular
    D. nervous

4. Which type of tissue causes the movement of structures in the body?
    A. epithelial
    B. connective
    C. muscular
    D. nervous

5. Which type of tissue is highly specialized to conduct nerve impulses?
    A. epithelial
    B. connective
    C. muscular
    D. nervous

6. Which type of tissue covers the surface of other tissues and forms the lining of body cavities?
    A. epithelial
    B. connective
    C. muscular
    D. nervous

7. Which type of tissue can form secretory cells in glands?
    A. epithelial
    B. connective
    C. muscular
    D. nervous

8. Intercalated discs are most likely to be observed in _____.
   A. skeletal muscle
   B. smooth muscle
   C. cardiac muscle
   D. all of the above

9. Which one of the following statements is **true**?
   A. Cardiac muscle fibers are not striated whereas skeletal muscle fibers are striated.
   B. Skeletal muscle fibers are not striated whereas cardiac muscle fibers are striated.
   C. Both cardiac muscle fibers and skeletal muscle fibers are striated.
   D. Skeletal muscle fibers exhibit branching while cardiac muscle fibers do not.

10. Which one of the following statements regarding muscle tissue is **false**?
    A. Cardiac muscle fibers are branched.
    B. Skeletal muscle fibers are long and multinucleated.
    C. Both cardiac muscle fibers and skeletal muscle fibers are striated.
    D. Smooth muscle fibers exhibit striations.

Name: _____ Class Time: _____ Class Day: _____

Complete skill checks 1-3.

Skill check #1

1. Name the tissue with several layers of closely packed flat cells.

    _____

2. Name one location of areolar connective tissue. _____.

Skill check # 2

1. Distinguish between the location and arrangement of chondrocytes and osteocytes.

    Location: _____

    _____

    Arrangement: _____

    _____

Skill check # 3

1. Contrast and compare the structure of the 3 types of muscle tissue.

    _____

    _____

    _____

    _____

    _____

    _____

    _____

    _____

6 Skeletal System: The Axial Division

OBJECTIVES:

After completing this laboratory you should be able to perform tasks listed below:

1. Identify the three bone groups of the axial skeleton.
2. Locate the major parts of a long bone.
3. Know the bones and sutures of the adult skull.
4. Identify the fontanels of the fetal skull.
5. List the subdivisions of the vertebral column and identify parts of a vertebra.
6. Identify bones of the rib cage.

The human skeleton is divided into two main parts: the axial skeleton and the appendicular skeleton. The **axial skeleton** includes all the flat or irregular bones that lie in the central region of the body. These axial bones are: bones of the skull, the hyoid bone, the vertebral column, and the rib cage (Figure. 6.1). The hyoid bone is suspended by ligaments and muscles below the mandible (Figure. 6.2). It is interesting to note that the hyoid bone does not articulate with any other bone. The **appendicular skeleton** includes the flat, long, and short bones that are added to the axial skeleton (Figure. 6.1).

© bluedoor, LLC

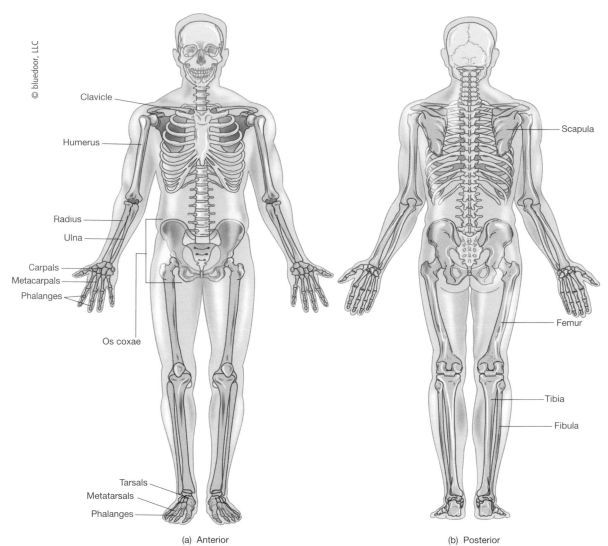

(a) Anterior   (b) Posterior

Figure 6.1: Human Skeleton. The bones of the appendicular skeleton
are colored purple to distinguish them from the bones of the axial skeleton.

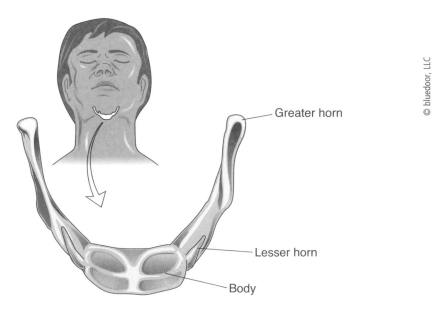

© bluedoor, LLC

Figure 6.2: The hyoid bone

A. Long Bone Anatomy

Activity 6.1: Identifying Features of a Long Bone

1. Study Figure 6.3.

2. Refer to Figure 6.3 and identify the features of the long bone provided.

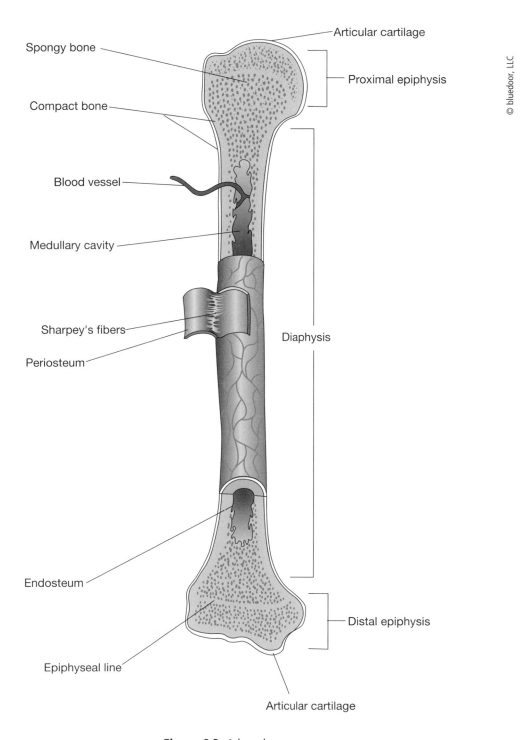

Figure 6.3: A long bone

B. Cranial Bones and Structures

Activity 6.2: Identifying Cranial Bones and Structures

1. Examine Figures 6. 1 and 6.4 carefully.

2. Refer to Figure 6.4 a–e and Table 6.1 as you identify the following cranial bones and structures on a model of the adult skull.

Frontal bone	**Sphenoid bone**
Parietal bones	-Greater wings & Lesser wings
Temporal bones	-Sella turcica
-Styloid process	-Optic canal
-Mandibular fossa	**Ethmoid bone**
-External auditory meatus	**Sutures:**
-Zygomatic process	**Coronal suture**
-Mastoid process	**Sagittal suture**
Occipital bone	**Lambdoid suture**
-Foramen Magnum	**Squamous suture**
-Occipital condyles	

C. Facial Bones and Structures

Activity 6.3: Identifying Facial Bones and Structures

1. Examine Figure 6.4 a–e carefully.

2. Refer to Figure 6.4 a–e and identify the following facial bones and structures on a model of the adult skull.

Maxilla	**Mandible**
Zygomatic bones	-Coronoid process
Lacrimal bones	-Mandibular condyle
Nasal bones	-Mental foramen
Palatine bones	-Body of mandible
	Vomer

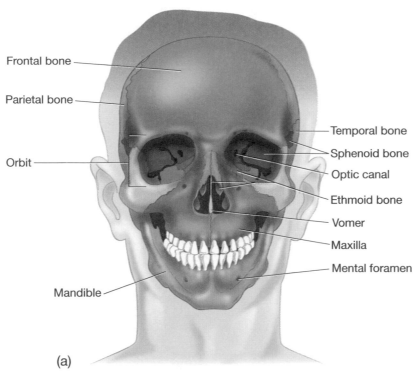

Frontal bone

Parietal bone

Orbit

Temporal bone

Sphenoid bone

Optic canal

Ethmoid bone

Vomer

Maxilla

Mental foramen

Mandible

© bluedoor, LLC

(a)

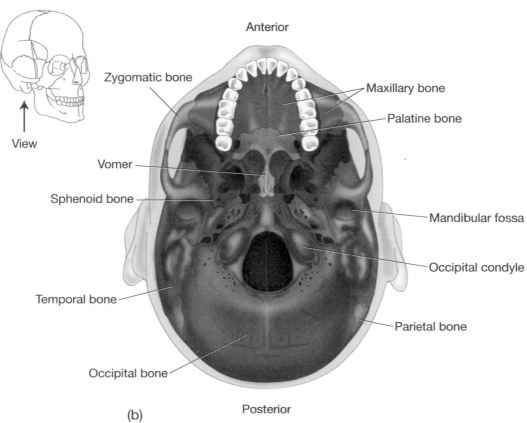

Anterior

View

Zygomatic bone

Maxillary bone

Palatine bone

Vomer

Sphenoid bone

Mandibular fossa

Temporal bone

Occipital condyle

Parietal bone

Occipital bone

Posterior

(b)

Figure 6.4 a & b: The human skull a) anterior b) inferior

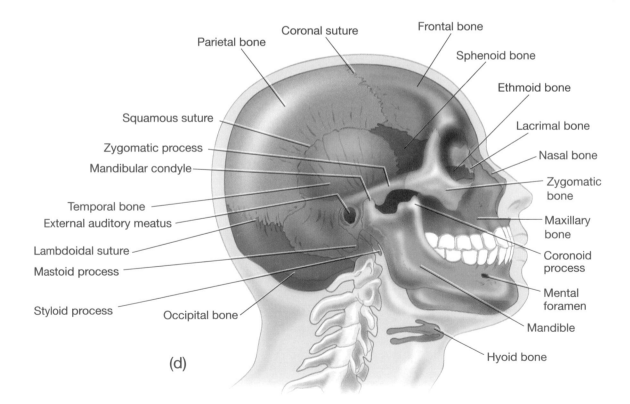

© bluedoor, LLC

Figure 6.4: The human skull c) superior, d) lateral.

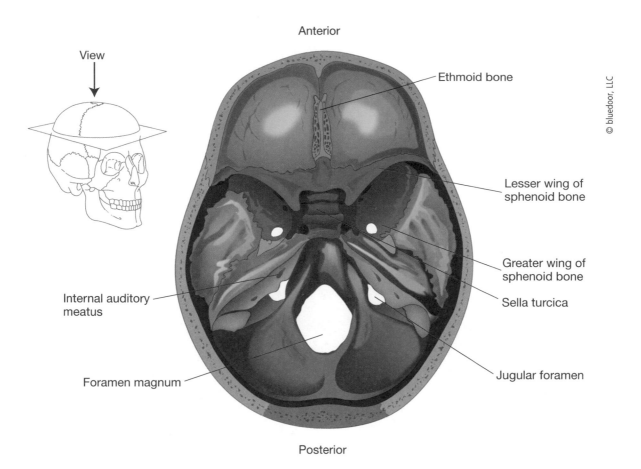

Figure 6.4e: The human skull. Floor of cranium.

Table 6.1: Surface Markings

Surface markings	Descriptions
Condyle	Smooth, rounded projection for articulation
Foramen	Hole or opening for passage of blood vessels and nerves
Fossa	Shallow depression for articulation or muscle attachment
Process	Projection
Spine	Pointed projection for muscle attachment

D. Fetal Skull

Activity 6.4: Identifying the Fontanels and Structures of a Fetal Skull

1. Examine Figures 6.4, 6.5 & 6.6 carefully.

2. Refer to Figures 6.5 & 6.6 and identify the following fontanels on a model of the fetal skull.
   Fontanels
   - -Anterior
   - -Posterior
   - -Anterolateral (Sphenoid)
   - -Posterolateral (Mastoid)

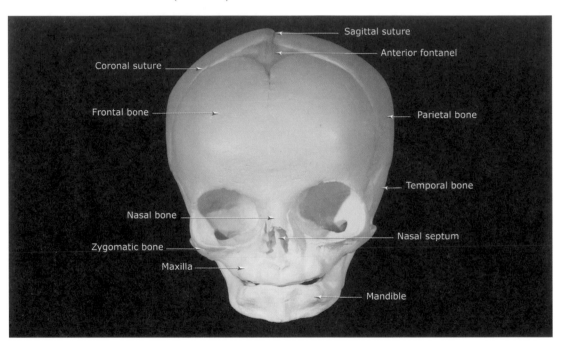

Figure 6.5: Anterior view of the Fetal skull

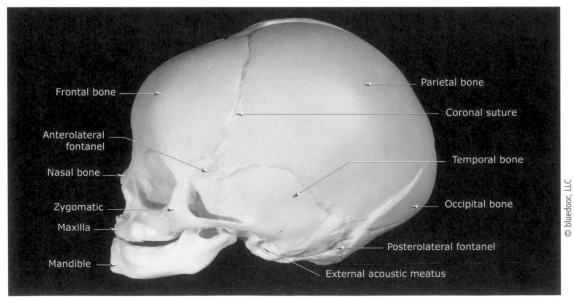

Figure 6.6: Lateral view of the fetal skull

E. The Vertebral Column

The vertebral column is a long, flexible structure that includes of a series of irregular bones called **vertebrae** in the **cervical**, **thoracic**, **lumbar**, **sacral**, and **coccygeal** regions of the body. There are 7 cervical vertebrae, 12 thoracic vertebrae, and 5 lumbar vertebrae. In adults, 5 sacral vertebrae fuse to form a single sacrum and 3 or sometimes 4 coccygeal vertebrae fuse to form the coccyx. The vertebral column has a **spinal canal** and **intervertebral foramina.** The spinal canal accommodates the spinal cord and **intervertebral foramina** provide a passage way for spinal nerves. **Intervertebral discs are composed** of fibrocartilage and exist between the cervical, thoracic, and lumbar vertebrae.

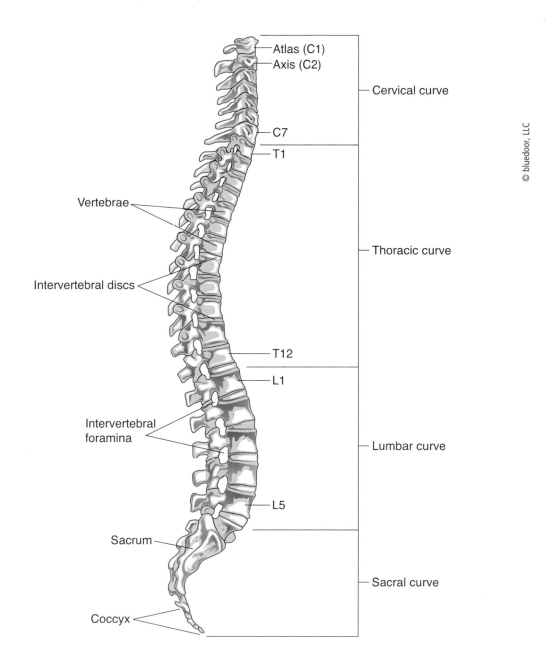

© bluedoor, LLC

Figure 6.7: Lateral view of vertebral column

Activity 6.5: Studying the Vertebral Column

Examine Figure 6.7 carefully.

1. Identify the labeled parts of Figure 6.7 on the vertebral column of the model articulated skeleton.

2. Refer to Figure 6.8. while you contrast the unique features of several disarticulated cervical, thoracic, and lumbar vertebrae.

3. Complete Table 6:2 showing some features of cervical, thoracic and lumbar vertebrae.

A cervical vertebra has a small body. The superior articular facet and the inferior articular process combined with the spinous process looks like a puppy with floppy ears. A thoracic vertebra has a medium sized body and looks like a giraffe with its decending spinous process being the nose. The lumbar vertebra looks like a lumbering moose, with the spinous process resembling a nose and the superior facets resembling antlers.

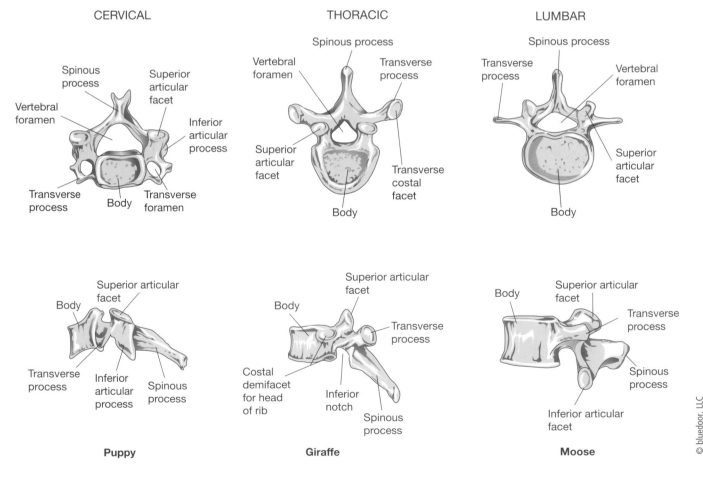

Figure 6.8: Typical cervical, thoracic, and lumbar vertebrae

© bluedoor, LLC

Table 6:2 Features of Cervical, Thoracic and Lumbar Vertebrae

Features	Cervical vertebra	Thoracic vertebra	Lumbar vertebra
Spinous process	Short & projects posteriorly		
Transverse process		Foramina absent	Foramina absent
Body		Larger than cervical	Massive and sturdy

F. The Thoracic Cage

The thoracic cage is composed of the bodies of thoracic vertebrae, the ribs, the sternum, and the costal cartilage. There are 12 pairs of ribs in males and females (Figure 6.9). Each rib is a long, curved, flat bone that articulates with the costal facets of the thoracic vertebrae. The first seven pairs of ribs are **true ribs** with their costal cartilages directly attached to the sternum. The last five pairs of ribs are **false ribs** and they do not attach directly to the sternum Rib pairs 11 and 12 are **floating ribs** they are neither attached to the sternum or to cartilage.

The **sternum** is a slender, flat bone located in the anterior thorax. It is composed of the fused manubrium, body of the sternum, and the xiphoid process. The **manubrium** is the superior region of the sternum that articulates with the two clavicles (collarbones) of the pectoral girdle and the first pair of ribs. There is a notch called the **jugular notch** or **suprasternal notch** at the superior border of the manubrium A **sternal angle** (angle of Louis) exists between the the manubrium and **body** of the sternum at the level of the second rib.. Rib pairs 2 -7 articulate with the body. The **xiphoid process** resembling a small sword forms the inferior portion of the sternum.(*xiph* = sword + *-oid* = resemblance to).

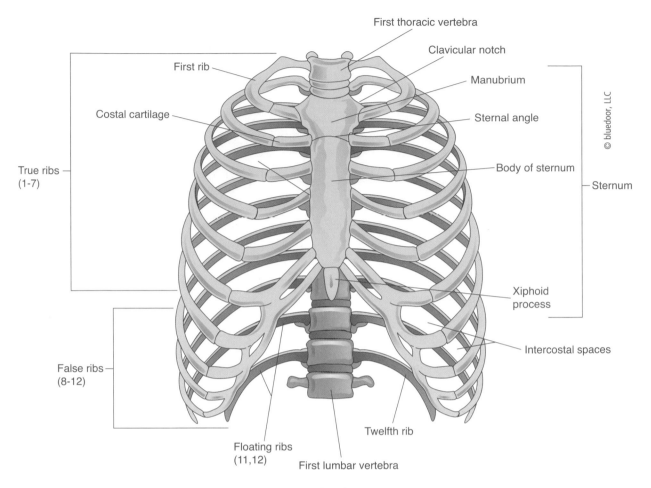

Figure 6.9: The rib cage

Activity 6.6: Studying the Thoracic Cage

Examine Figure 6.9 carefully.

Identify the labeled parts of Figure 6.9 on a model of an articulated skeleton.

CHAPTER REVIEW

Complete the following sentences.

1. The large, flat anterior cranial bone is called the _____ bone.

2. The squamosal suture is an immoveable joint located between the _____ and _____ bones.

3. All the bones that lie along the central region of the body are called the _____ _____.

4. The anterior fontanel of the fetal skull is located between the _____ and _____ bones.

5. The _____ are located at both ends of a long bone.

6. The coronoid process may be found on the _____ bone.

7. The _____ bone has a greater and lesser wing.

8. The mastoid process and zygomatic process are parts of the _____ bone.

9. Transverse foramina are unique features of _____ vertebrae.

10. Ribs articulate with costal facets of _____ vertebrae.

Name: _____ Class Time: _____ Class Day: _____

Complete skill checks 1 – 3.

Skill check #1

Label the parts indicated on the diagram of the long bone shown below.

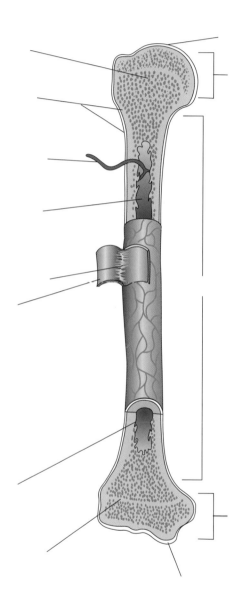

Skill check #2

Study the adult cranial bones, their structures, and their sutures. Then, study the fontanels of the fetal skull. Your instructor will ask you to identify specific cranial bones and structures. You may also be asked to compare and contrast features of the adult skull with features of the fetal skull.

Skill check #3

Study the structures of the vertebral column and the thoracic cage. Your instructor will test your knowledge of these structures.

7 Skeletal System: The Appendicular Skeleton and Joints

OBJECTIVES:

After completing this laboratory you should be able to perform tasks listed below.

1. Recognize selected bone markings.
2. Identify bones of different regions of the appendicular skeleton.
3. Distinguish between the male and female pelvis.
4. Classify joints according to their structural and functional classifications.
5. Describe the general structure of a synovial joint.
6. Name six categories of synovial joints and give an example of each category.
7. Demonstrate types of joint movement.

The appendicular skeleton includes bones that form the pectoral girdle, the upper limbs, the pelvic girdle, and the lower limbs. Special markings on the bones facilitate muscle attachment and articulations with adjacent bones. Many of the surface markings can be used for bone identification. Table 7.1 shows selected surface markings and their descriptions.

Table 7.1: Surface Markings

Surface markings	Descriptions
Condyle	Smooth, rounded projection for articulation
Crest	Ridge for muscle attachment
Foramen	Hole or opening for passage of blood vessels and nerves
Fossa	Shallow depression for articulation or muscle attachment
Head	Large, proximal prominence for articulation
Process	Projection
Spine	Pointed projection for muscle attachment
Trochanter	Large projection for muscle attachment unique to femur
Tubercle	Small, rounded projection for muscle attachment
Tuberosity	Rough, raised surface for muscle attachment

A. Bones of the Pectoral Girdles

The pectoral girdles are paired and attach the upper limbs to the axial skeleton. In addition, they provide sites for attaching muscles of the shoulder and brachium (arm). Each pectoral girdle is composed of an anterior clavicle and a posterior scapula.

Students are required to work in pairs on activities 7.1 to 7.7.

Activity 7.1: Studying Bones of the Pectoral Girdle

Refer to Figure 7.1 and identify the clavicle (collarbone) and scapula (shoulder blade) on a model of the human skeleton.

Refer to Figures 7.2 and 7.3. Then, identify the main parts of models of a disarticulated clavicle and scapula. On the scapula, note the location of the **acromion, coracoid process, glenoid cavity/fossa, lateral (axillary) border, medial (vertebral) border,** s**pine, subscapular fossa, suprascapular notch, supraspinous fossa and the infraspinous fossa.**

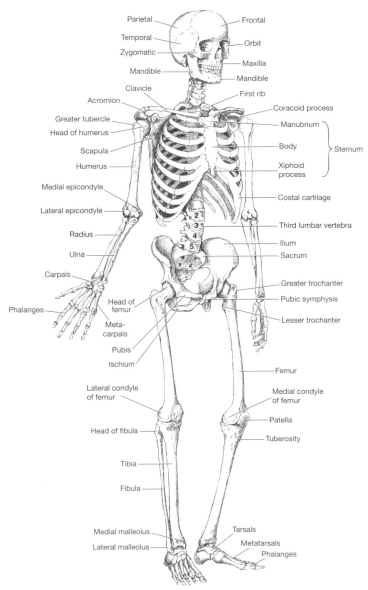

© bluedoor, LLC

Figure 7.1: Human skeleton

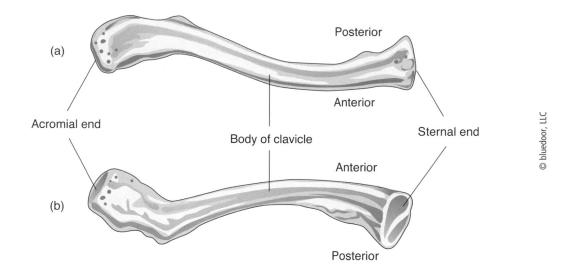

Figure 7.2: Clavicle: a) superior view b) inferior view

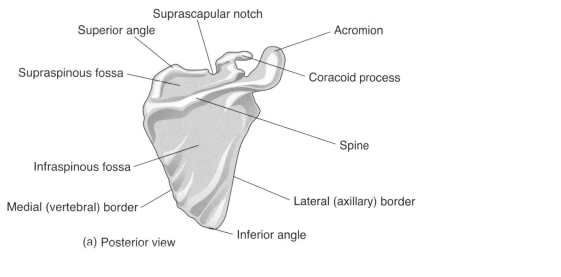

(a) Posterior view

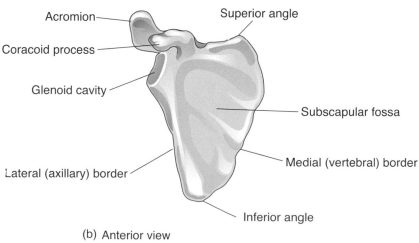

(b) Anterior view

Figure 7.3: Scapula: (a) posterior view, (b) anterior view

© bluedoor, LLC

B. Bones of the Upper Limb

Each upper limb includes an arm (brachium), forearm (antebrachium), and hand. A hand contains a wrist (carpus), a body (metacarpus), and fingers (digits). Each arm has one bone known as the humerus. Each forearm contains one lateral bone known as the radius and one medial bone known as the ulna. The hand has carpal bones in the wrist, metacarpal bones in the body, and the phalanges in the fingers.

Activity 7.2: Studying Upper Limb Bones

On a model of the human skeleton, identify the **humerus**, **radius**, **ulna**, **carpals**, **metacarpals**, and **phalanges** that are shown in Figure 7.1.

Examine the model of a disarticulated skeleton and identify the bone markings of the **humerus**, **radius**, **ulna**, **carpals**, **metacarpals**, and **phalanges** that are shown in Figures 7.4 - 7.6.

Palpate the **greater** and **lesser tubercles** of the humerus, the **olecranon process** of the ulna as well as the **styloid processes** of the radius and ulna on your body.

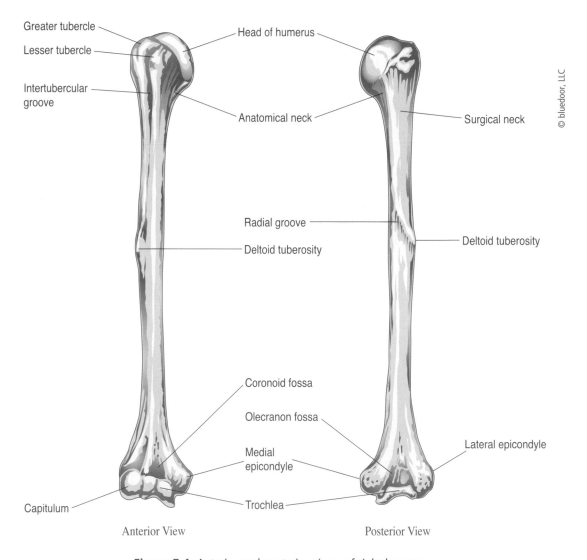

Anterior View   Posterior View

Figure 7.4: Anterior and posterior views of right humerus

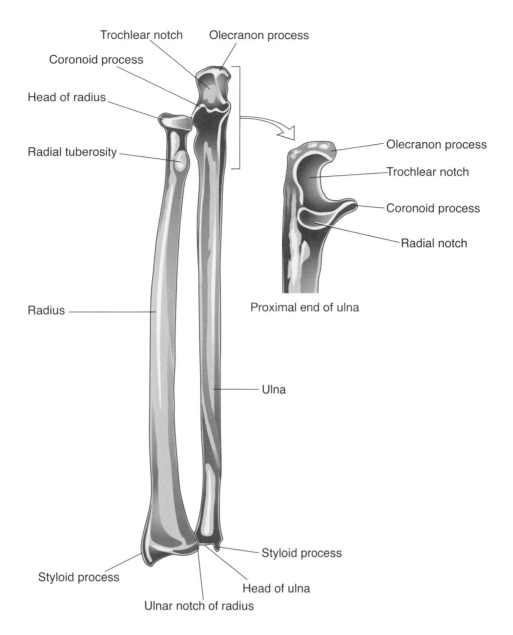

Figure 7.5: Anterior views of right radius and ulna

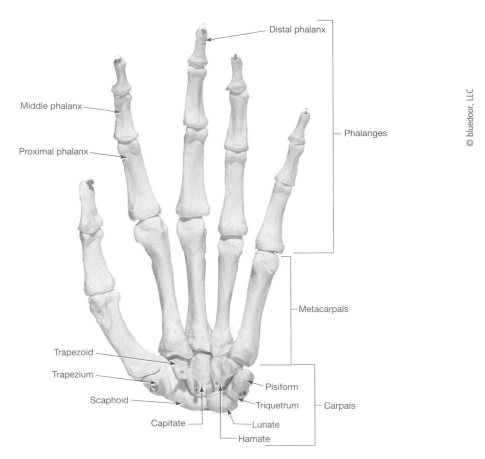

Figure 7.6: Bones of the left hand (anterior or palmar view)

C. Bones of the Pelvic Girdle

The **pelvic girdle** contains two **hip bones** or os coxae (os = bone + coxa = hip) that support the superior parts of the body and provide sites for attachment of the hip and thigh muscles. Each hip bone is composed of three bones known as the ilium, the ischium, and the pubis that fuse during childhood. These bones form a deep depression known as the **acetabulum** that facilitates articulation of an os coxa with the head of the femur at the hip joint. In each hip bone, there is a large hole known as the **obturator foramen** that provides a passage way for nerves and blood vessels.

In adults, two hip bones articulate anteriorly to form a slightly movable cartilaginous joint known as the pubic symphysis. Posteriorly, these bones articulate with the sacrum to form the sacroiliac joints. A male's pelvic girdle is thick, rough, and almost vertical. It has a heart-shaped pelvic inlet and the angle of the pubic arch is 90º or less. In contrast, a female's pelvic girdle is fairly thin, smooth, and tilts towards the back. The pelvic inlet of the female's pelvic girdle is round or oval and the angle of the pubic arch is greater than 90 º. Overall, the female's pelvic girdle is designed to facilitate childbirth.

Activity 7.3: Studying Bones of the Pelvic Girdle

Examine a model of the human skeleton and identify the main parts of the **pelvic girdle** that are shown in Figure 7.1.

Examine the pelvic girdle from the model of a disarticulated skeleton and identify the bone markings of a **hip bone** that are shown in Figure 7.7.

Palpate the **iliac crest** and the **anterior superior iliac spine** on your body.

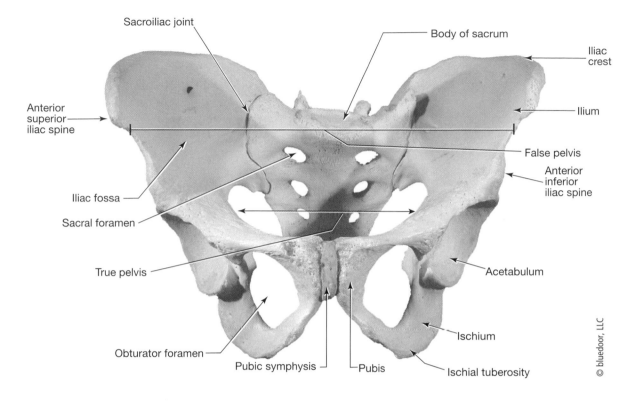

Sacroiliac joint

Body of sacrum

Iliac crest

Anterior superior iliac spine

Ilium

False pelvis

Anterior inferior iliac spine

Iliac fossa

Sacral foramen

True pelvis

Acetabulum

Obturator foramen

Ischium

Pubic symphysis

Pubis

Ischial tuberosity

© bluedoor, LLC

Figure 7.7: Pelvic girdle

D. Bones of the Lower Limb

Each lower limb includes a thigh bone or femur, a kneecap or patella, a medial tibia and lateral fibula in the leg, and 26 bones of the foot. Each foot includes tarsal bones that form the ankle or tarsus, metatarsal bones that form the body of the foot, and phalanges that form the toes. The medial bulge (medial malleolus) at the distal end of the tibia forms the medial aspect of the ankle and the lateral bulge (lateral malleolus) on the fibula forms the lateral aspect of the ankle. (Figure 7.9)

Activity 7.4: Studying Lower Limb Bones

On a model of the human skeleton, identify the **femur, patella, tibia, fibula, tarsals, metatarsals, and phalanges** that are shown in Figure 7.1.

Examine the model of a disarticulated skeleton and identify the bone markings of the **femur, patella, tibia, fibula, tarsals, metatarsals, and phalanges** that are shown in Figures 7.8 - 7.11.

Palpate your own body to feel the **greater trochanter** of the femur; the **patella**; the **tibial tuberosity**; the **medial malleolus** of the tibia; the **lateral malleolus** of the fibula; as well as the **talus** and **calcaneus** of the foot.

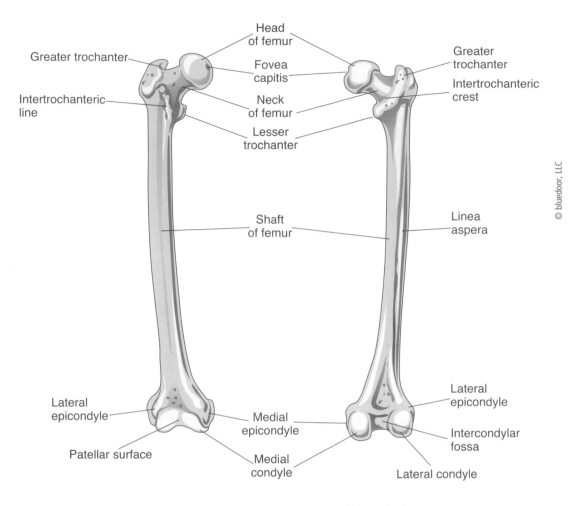

Head of femur

Fovea capitis

Greater trochanter

Intertrochanteric line

Neck of femur

Lesser trochanter

Greater trochanter

Intertrochanteric crest

Shaft of femur

Linea aspera

Lateral epicondyle

Patellar surface

Medial epicondyle

Medial condyle

Lateral epicondyle

Intercondylar fossa

Lateral condyle

© bluedoor, LLC

Figure 7.8: Anterior and posterior views of the right femur

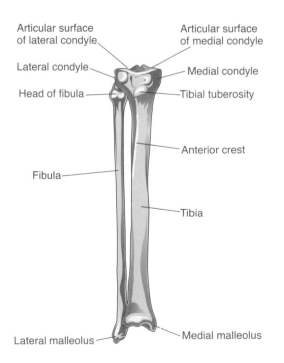

Articular surface of lateral condyle

Lateral condyle

Head of fibula

Articular surface of medial condyle

Medial condyle

Tibial tuberosity

Anterior crest

Fibula

Tibia

Lateral malleolus

Medial malleolus

© bluedoor, LLC

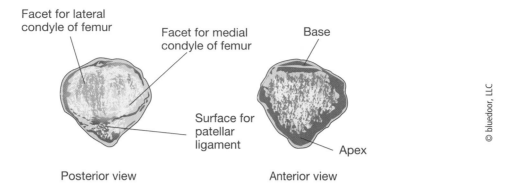

Facet for lateral condyle of femur

Facet for medial condyle of femur

Base

Surface for patellar ligament

Apex

Posterior view

Anterior view

© bluedoor, LLC

Figure 7.9: Anterior view of the right tibia and fibula articulated
Figure 7.10: Anterior and posterior views of the patella

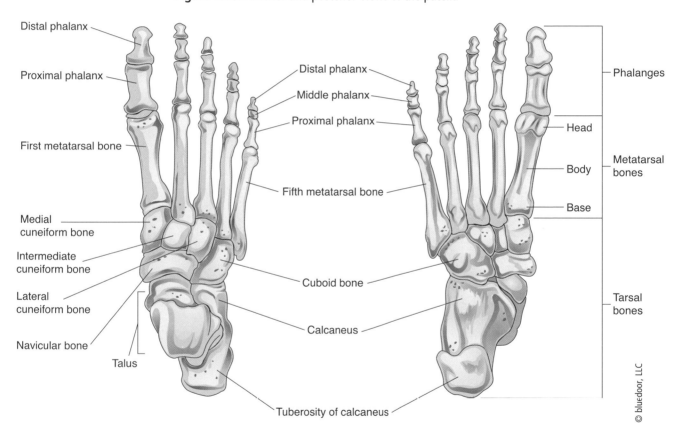

Distal phalanx

Proximal phalanx

Distal phalanx

Middle phalanx

Proximal phalanx

Phalanges

First metatarsal bone

Head

Body

Fifth metatarsal bone

Metatarsal bones

Base

Medial cuneiform bone

Intermediate cuneiform bone

Cuboid bone

Lateral cuneiform bone

Tarsal bones

Navicular bone

Talus

Calcaneus

Tuberosity of calcaneus

© bluedoor, LLC

Figure 7.11: Dorsal and plantar views of the right foot

E. JOINTS AND MOVEMENTS

Joints or **articulations** connect bones to other bones, cartilage or teeth. Two alternative methods are used to classify joints. One method is based on the structural components of a joint and the other is based on the function. Different categories of movable joints allow the human body to display a diverse range of movements.

Structural Classification

Joints may be composed of dense fibrous connective tissue, cartilage, or bone. Alternatively, some joints have a cavity that contains synovial fluid. Hence, joints are classified structurally into four categories: a) **fibrous joints** b) c**artilaginous joints c) bony joints d) synovial joints.**

Fibrous joints include the sutures between the cranial bones, joint between the manubrium and sternal body, joints between teeth and their sockets in the maxilla and mandibles, as well as the distal joint between the tibia and fibula. **A fibrous joint** has a rich supply of collagen fibers that connect two bones firmly together. There is no space between the two bones and little or no movement is allowed.

Cartilaginous joints have hyaline cartilage or fibrocartilage between bones. No space exists between two bones at a **cartilaginous joint** and limited movement is allowed. The intervertebral discs and the pubic symphysis are examples of cartilaginous joints.

Bony joints have osseous tissue (bone) between bones. No space exists between two bones at a bony joint and no movement is allowed. The joints between the sacral vertebrae and between the bones of the coccyx are examples of bony joints.

A synovial joint has a **synovial cavity** between two bones. There is an **articular capsule** around the synovial cavity and articular cartilage covers the ends of bones that protrude into the cavity. Each articular capsule is composed of an outer **fibrous capsule** as well as an inner **synovial membrane.** The synovial membrane secretes a viscous and slippery synovial fluid that lubricates articular cartilage and minimizes friction in joints. Synovial joints include the hip, shoulder, elbow, and knee joints.

Activity 7.5: Structural Classification of Joints

Carefully examine models of the shoulder, elbow, wrist, hand as well as the joints of an articulated skeleton.

On a model of the human skeleton, locate the joints indicated on Figure 7.12.

Use Table 7.2 as a guide in order to note the locations and specific features of the six types of synovial joints that exist in the human body.

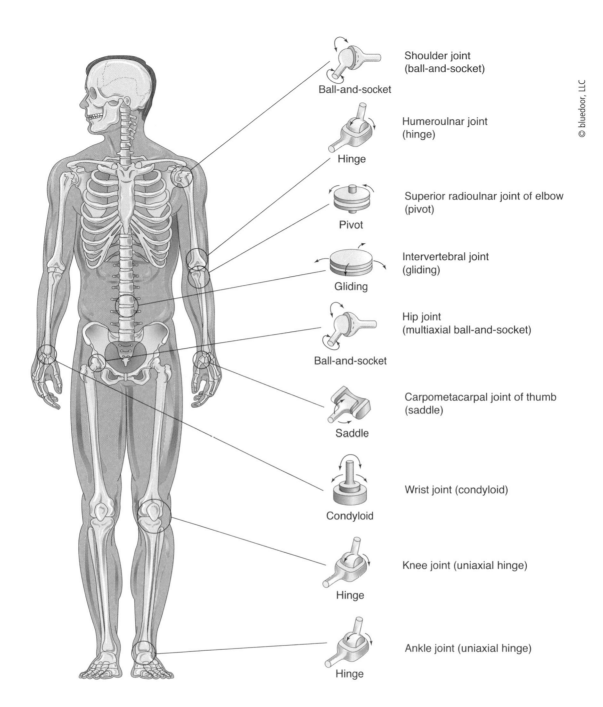

Shoulder joint
(ball-and-socket)

Ball-and-socket

Humeroulnar joint
(hinge)

Hinge

Superior radioulnar joint of elbow
(pivot)

Pivot

Intervertebral joint
(gliding)

Gliding

Hip joint
(multiaxial ball-and-socket)

Ball-and-socket

Carpometacarpal joint of thumb
(saddle)

Saddle

Wrist joint (condyloid)

Condyloid

Knee joint (uniaxial hinge)

Hinge

Ankle joint (uniaxial hinge)

Hinge

Figure 7.12: Structural classification of joints

Functional Classification

Joints may be classified based on their functional characteristics or their ability to move. Immovable joints are **synarthroses** (syn = union + arthro = joint). Sutures between the cranial bones and the joints between teeth and their sockets in the jawbones are examples of **synarthroses**. Joints that allow slight movement are **amphiarthroses** (amphi = two sides). Intervertebral discs and pubic symphyses are examples of amphiarthroses. Freely moveable joints are **diarthroses** (di = apart). The shoulder, elbow, hip, and knee are examples of diarthroses.

Activity 7.6: Identifying Joints Based on Their Function

Locate the synarthroses, amphiarthroses, and diarthroses on the model of a skeleton.

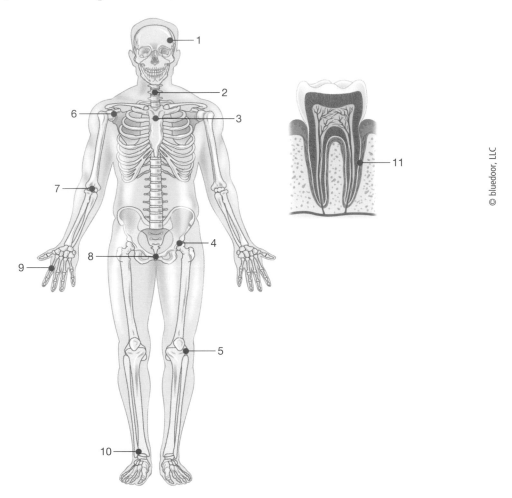

© bluedoor, LLC

Figure 7.13: Functional classification of joints

Synovial Joints

Synovial joints are diarthroses (freely movable). Six categories of synovial joints with unique features exist in the human body. Figure 7.14 illustrates a) the shoulder joint; b) hip joint; and c) knee joint. Table 7.2 shows features and movements of each category of synovial joints.

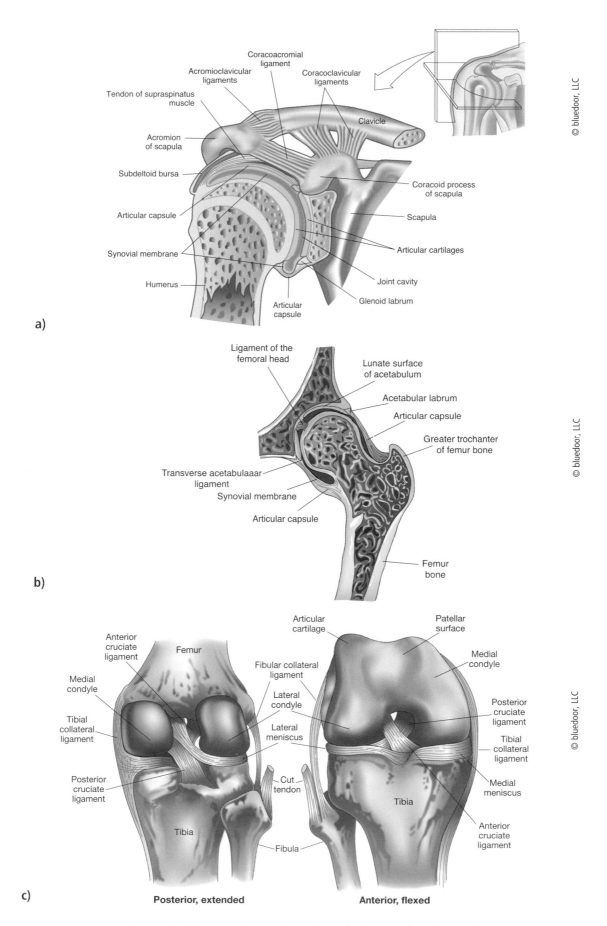

Figure 7.14: Synovial joints: a) shoulder joint b) hip joint c) knee joint

Table 7.2: Features and Movements of Synovial Joints

Synovial joints	Features	Movements
Ball and socket: Shoulder & hip joints	A ball-shaped head of a limb bone articulates with a cuplike depression of a girdle	Angular movements and rotation
Condyloid: Radiocarpal joints	Condyle (oval convex projection) articulates with an ellipsoidal depression	Angular movements
Hinge: Elbow joint& knee joints	The convex surface of a bone articulates with the concave surface of another bone	Flexion and extension
Pivot: Atlantoaxial & radioulnar joints	The rounded surface of a bone fits into a depression or foramen	Rotation
Planar/gliding: Intercarpal joints	Flat or slightly curved smooth surfaces articulate	Gliding
Saddle: Thumb metacarpal joint	A saddle-shaped concavity articulates with a convex surface	Angular movements

Angular movements include abduction (movement away from midline), adduction (movement toward midline), circumduction, extension, and flexion.

Circumduction refers to joint movement that combines flexion, abduction, adduction and extension that looks similar to rotation.

Extension occurs when the angle between bones increases. Hyperextension occurs if the angle increases beyond 180º.

Flexion occurs when the angle between bones decreases.

Gliding refers to movement of smooth surfaces back and forth and/or side to side over each other.

Rotation refers to movement on a pivot in a circular motion.

Supination causes palm movement from posterior to anterior.

Pronation causes palm movement from anterior to posterior.

Inversion results in sole movement in a medial direction.

Eversion results in sole movement in a lateral direction.

Dorsiflexion refers to upward (dorsal) movement of the ankle joint so toes point up.

Plantar flexion refers to movement of the ankle joint downward so toes point down.

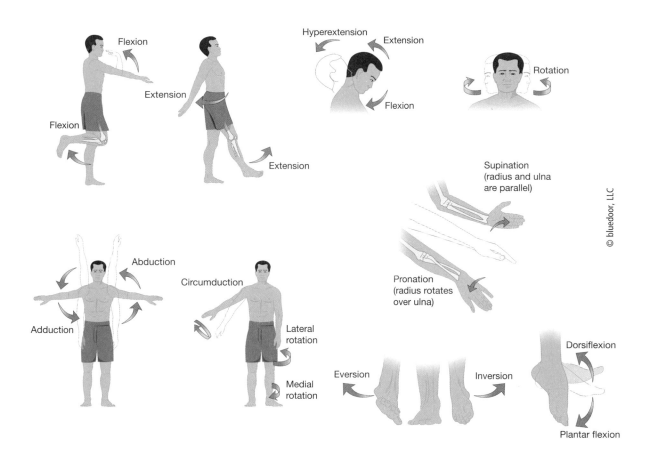

© bluedoor, LLC

Figure 7.15: Joint movements

Activity 7.7: Movements at Synovial Joints

1. Refer to Table 7.2 and Figure 7.15. Then, demonstrate the possible movements at each type of synovial joint to your partner.
2. Use an articulated skeleton to demonstrate different joint movements.
3. Palpate examples of the following categories of synovial joints on your body.
   a. **Ball-and-socket joint**: Feel the **glenohumeral joint** (shoulder joint) where the ball-shaped head of the humerus articulates with the glenoid fossa of the scapula.
   b. **Condyloid joint**: Feel one of the joints in the hand between the base of a finger and a metacarpal.
   c. **Hinge joint**: Feel your elbow as you flex and extend your arm.
   d. **Pivot joint**: Twist the forearm back and forth from a supine to a prone position. This twisting movement is possible because the radioulnar joint is a pivot joint.
   e. **Planar or gliding joint**: Elevate your arm and feel the gliding back-and forth movement of the **acromioclavicular joint** between the acromion and the clavicle.
   f. **Saddle joint**: Feel the joint between the thumb and the trapezium of the wrist.

CHAPTER REVIEW

1. A fossa is a _____.
    A. small rounded projection   C. large hole
    B. shallow depression   D. prominent ridge

2. Greater and lesser tubercles are bone markings of the _____.
    A. femur   C. scapula
    B. tibia   D. humerus

3. A broken acromion often prevents proper articulation of the scapula with the
    _____.
    A. pubis   C. sternum
    B. ischium   D. clavicle

4. The head of the radius articulates _____.
    A. proximally with the humerus   C. proximally with the scapula
    B. distally with the tarsals   D. distally with the tibia

5. Elbow joints are examples of _____.
    A. cartilaginous joints   C. fibrous joints
    B. amphiarthroses   D. diarthroses

6. A tibia articulates _____.
    A. proximally with the pelvic girdle   C. proximally with the scapula
    B. distally with the tarsals   D. distally with the carpals

7. A medial malleolus is a part of the _____.
    A. femur   C. scapula
    B. tibia   D. fibula

8. The thigh bone is the _____.
    A. calcaneus   C. tibia
    B. talus   D. femur

9. Phalanges are bones of the _____.
    A. palms   C. feet
    B. fingers and toes   D. feet and toes

10. Which one of the following descriptions refers to a female's pelvic girdle?
    A. It is thick, rough, and almost vertical.
    B. It has a round or oval pelvic inlet.
    C. It has a heart-shaped pelvic inlet.
    D. The angle of the pubic arch is 90° or less.

Name: _____ Class Time: _____ Class Day: _____

Complete skill checks 1 – 3.

Skill check #1

a)   Name the 4 groups of bones that form the appendicular skeleton.

i)   _____

ii) _____

iii) _____

iv) _____

Complete Table 7.3

Table 7.3: Appendicular Bones, Characteristic Markings, and Their Locations

Bone	Marking	Location of marking
	Glenoid Cavity	Lateral
Humerus	Greater tubercle	
Radius	Head	
	Olecranon process	Proximal
	Greater trochanter	Proximal and Lateral
Tibia	Tibial Tuberosity	
Fibula		Distal

Skill check #2

Examine the pelvis of an articulated skeleton and identify it as either male or female. Circle your answer. (*Male / Female*)

Describe 3 ways in which the pelvic girdle of a male differs from that of a female.

_____

_____

_____

Skill check #3

Identify each joint in Figure 7.13 and write fibrous, cartilaginous, or synovial beside the number used to indicate the joint. Number 1 is done for you.

1. _____Fibrous_____   7. _____

2. _____   8. _____

3. _____   9. _____

4. _____   10. _____

5. _____   11. _____

6. _____

.

8 Muscles I

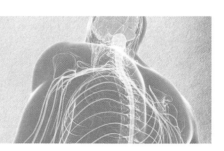

OBJECTIVES:

After completing this laboratory you should be able to perform tasks listed below.

1. Name and state an action of specified muscles of the head and neck.
2. Name and state an action of specified muscles of the trunk.

There are more than 600 skeletal muscles in the human body. However, you are required to study less than 70 of these muscles in this lab. It is important for you to understand how muscles are named. In order to facilitate the learning process, the muscles are categorized on the basis of their location and primary body movement. In this unit, a tabular format is used to describe the location, point of origin, point of insertion, and primary action of major muscles. Also, all the muscles that you will learn in this unit are illustrated in Figures 8.1 and 8.2.

A muscle that causes movement is called a prime mover, or **agonist**. A muscle that acts in an opposite way to the agonist is referred to as an **antagonistic** muscle and is called an **antagonist**. When an agonist is active (contracting), the antagonist is relaxed. A good example of antagonistic muscular action to consider is flexing your elbow. You contract your biceps brachii, which is a prime mover during elbow flexion, and you relax your triceps because it's the antagonist to the biceps brachii.

We also have muscles called **synergists** in our body. A synergist assists the action of an agonist. So, both the agonist and the synergist are in synergy with the movement. A **fixator** is a synergist that fixes or immobilizes the origin of the agonist for smooth motion.

The **origin** of a muscle refers to the point of attachment of a muscle to an immovable structure such as a bone. The attachment site of a muscle to a moveable bone or other moveable structure such as the skin is called the **insertion**. The movement that a muscle performs is called a contraction. The action of a muscle refers to the movement of the bone during that contraction.

A. Naming Muscles

Learning the names of almost 70 muscles is a challenging task. Names of muscles are based on Latin or Greek words. Therefore, understanding the meaning of the words will help you to study the muscles. Below are examples of terms that relate to naming muscles based on their location, size, shape, direction or orientation of muscle fibers, action, origin, and insertion.

Example of terms used to name muscles based on:

1. Location: Some muscles are named for their location.
   For example: rectus abdominis (*rectus* = straight + *abdominis* = abdomen)
   abdominis – abdomen
   brachium – arm
   femoris – thigh
   gluteus – buttock
   pectoralis – chest

2. Size: Some muscle names describe their relative muscle size.
   For example: gluteus minimus (*gluteus* = buttock + *minimus* = smallest)
   brevis – short
   longus – long
   maximus – largest
   minimus – smallest

3. Shape: Some muscles are named according to their shape.
   For example: the deltoid (deltoid = triangular shape) muscle of the arm.
   deltoid – triangular
   trapezius – trapezoid
   piriformis-shaped like a pear

4. Direction of fibers: Some muscles are named according to the direction in which
   their fibers run.
   For example: external oblique (*external* = outside + **oblique** = slanted)
   rectus – straight or parallel
   transverse - at right angles or perpendicular
   oblique – slanted (neither perpendicular nor parallel)

5. Origin: Some muscles are named after the number of points of origin or heads.
   For example: the triceps brachii (tri = three + ceps = heads, brachii = arm) is a muscle with three origins.
   bi – two
   tri – three
   quad – four
   ceps – head

6. Action (movement produced): Some muscles are named according to a general
   movement they produce during contraction.
   For example: extensor digitorum (*extensor* = extend + *digitorum* = fingers)
   extensor – to spread or stretch to open an angle
   flexor – to bend a body part to close an angle
   abductor - to draw or spread away from the midline of the body
   adductor – to move towards the midline of the body

7. Location of origin and insertion: Some muscles are named according to the location
   of their origin and insertion.
   For example: the sternocleidomastoid (sterno = sternum + cleido = clavicle + mastoid = breast- like) has origins on the sternum and clavicle and inserts on the mastoid process of the temporal bone.
   sterno – sternum
   cleido – clavicle
   mastoid - resembling a breast

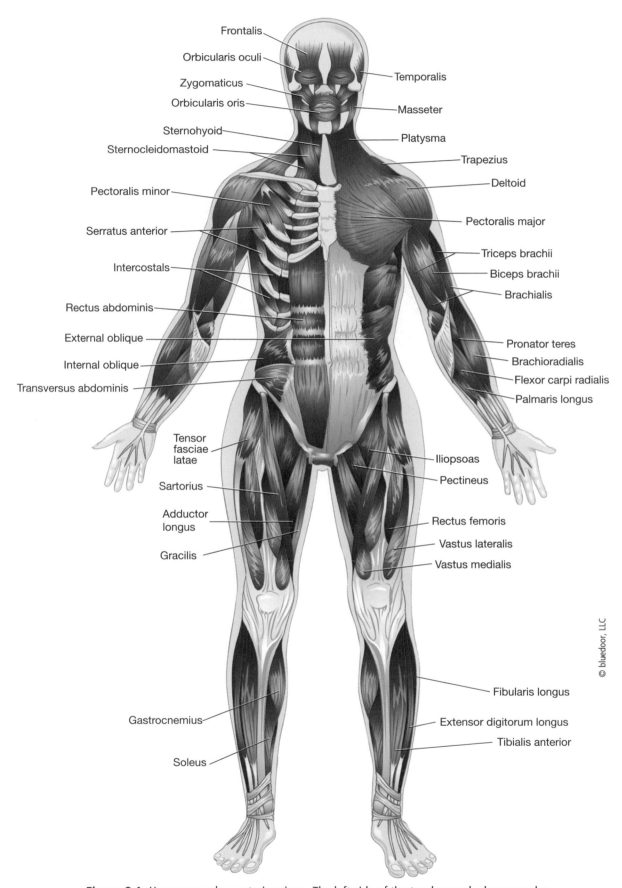

Frontalis

Orbicularis oculi

Zygomaticus

Orbicularis oris

Sternohyoid

Sternocleidomastoid

Pectoralis minor

Serratus anterior

Intercostals

Rectus abdominis

External oblique

Internal oblique

Transversus abdominis

Tensor fasciae latae

Sartorius

Adductor longus

Gracilis

Gastrocnemius

Soleus

Temporalis

Masseter

Platysma

Trapezius

Deltoid

Pectoralis major

Triceps brachii

Biceps brachii

Brachialis

Pronator teres

Brachioradialis

Flexor carpi radialis

Palmaris longus

Iliopsoas

Pectineus

Rectus femoris

Vastus lateralis

Vastus medialis

Fibularis longus

Extensor digitorum longus

Tibialis anterior

© bluedoor, LLC

Figure 8.1: Human muscles, anterior view. The left side of the trunk reveals deep muscles.

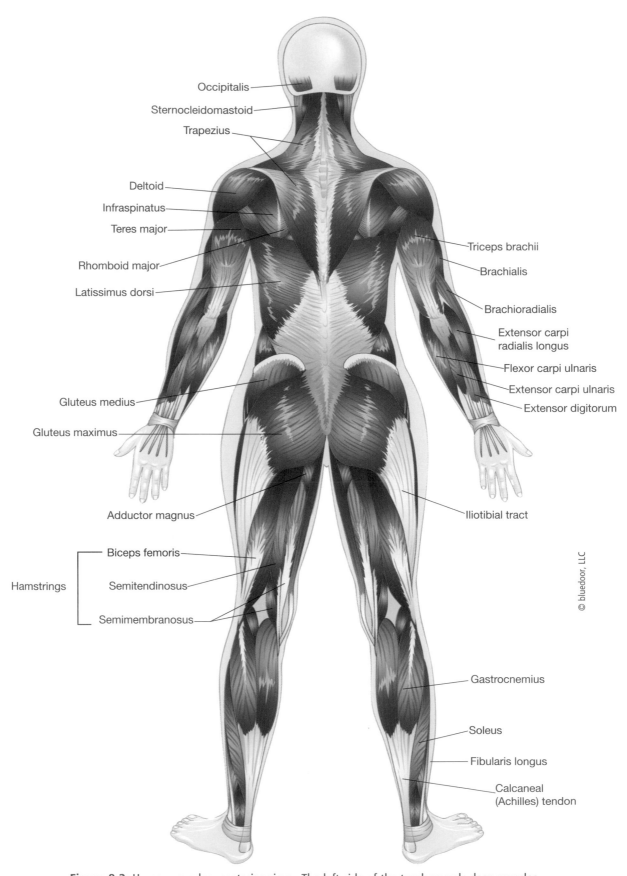

Occipitalis

Sternocleidomastoid

Trapezius

Deltoid

Infraspinatus

Teres major

Rhomboid major

Latissimus dorsi

Triceps brachii

Brachialis

Brachioradialis

Extensor carpi
radialis longus

Flexor carpi ulnaris

Extensor carpi ulnaris

Extensor digitorum

Gluteus medius

Gluteus maximus

Iliotibial tract

Adductor magnus

Hamstrings {
Biceps femoris

Semitendinosus

Semimembranosus

Gastrocnemius

Soleus

Fibularis longus

Calcaneal
(Achilles) tendon

© bluedoor, LLC

Figure 8.2: Human muscles, posterior view. The left side of the trunk reveals deep muscles.

Activity 8.1: Naming Muscles

Review the information in the preceding sections. Then, answer the following questions.

1. Refer to Figures 8.1 and 8.2 and provide an example of a muscle, not included in the preceding discussion, that derived its name based on location.

_____

2. How many heads of origin does the quadriceps femoris have?

_____

3. What can you determine about the deltoid on the basis of its name?

_____

4. On the basis of its name, state the function of the extensor digitorum?

_____

B. Muscles of the Head and Neck

Muscles of the head are involved in facial expression, moving the jaw for talking and chewing (mastication), or moving the eye during vision. The muscles of facial expression are unique because they insert into the skin, or on other muscles, instead of inserting on bones. By moving the skin of the face, they enable you to frown or smile, stare or glare, etc. The muscles that move the jaw are powerful and are attached bone to bone. The muscles moving the eyeballs extend from the inside of the orbit to insert on each eyeball. Each eyeball has six extrinsic muscles.

The head is moved by many of the muscles of the neck. Muscles that move the tongue and the throat during speaking or swallowing are attached to the hyoid bone. The muscles moving the head are long, and are located posterior or lateral to the head. The muscles connected to the hyoid bone are small, anterior muscles.

Activity 8.2: Muscles of the Head and Neck

Study all the muscles of the head and neck listed in Tables 8.1, 8.2, and 8.3 by identifying them on models, and charts that are available in your lab.

Familiarize yourself with the actions of these muscles. Use Figures 8.3, 8.4, 8.5, and 8.6 as helpful guides.

Answer the questions 1-3 in this section.

Table 8.1: Facial Muscles

Muscle	Description	Origin	Insertion	Action
Occipitofrontalis (Epicranius)	covers the top of the skull	occipitalis on occipital and temporal bones frontalis on cranial aponeurosis	occipitalis on cranial aponeurosis frontalis on skin over the eyes and the nose	occipitalis raises scalp frontalis raises brows
Orbicularis oculi	circular sphincter muscle of eyelids	frontal and maxillary bones	inside of eyelid	closes eyes
Orbicularis oris	circular sphincter muscle of mouth	maxillary and mandible	skin and muscle around mouth	closes mouth; protrudes lips
Zygomaticus	consists of two thin muscles, from corner of the mouth to cheek	zygomatic bone	skin and muscle at corner of mouth	elevates lateral corners of the mouth to smile
Platysma	thin, superficial muscle of the neck	fascia of thorax	lower mandible, skin and muscle	depress jaw and lower lip to turn the mouth downward

Table 8.2: Muscles of Mastication

Muscle	Description	Origin	Insertion	Action
Masseter	covers the lateral aspect of the ramus of mandible	zygomatic arch and maxillary	angle and ramus of mandible	closes jaw; elevates mandible
Temporalis	fan-shaped muscle on the lateral head	temporal fossa of temporal bone	coronoid process of mandible	closes jaw; elevates and retracts jaw
Buccinator	main muscle of the cheek deep to the masseter	posterior maxillary and mandible	orbicularis oris	draws corner of mouth laterally (as in whistling)

Table 8.3: Muscle that Moves the Head

Muscle	Description	Origin	Insertion	Action
Sternocleido-mastoid	two headed muscle located deep to platysma	manubrium of sternum and the clavicle	mastoid process of temporal bone and the occipital bone	bilaterally—flexion of the neck unilaterally—turns the head

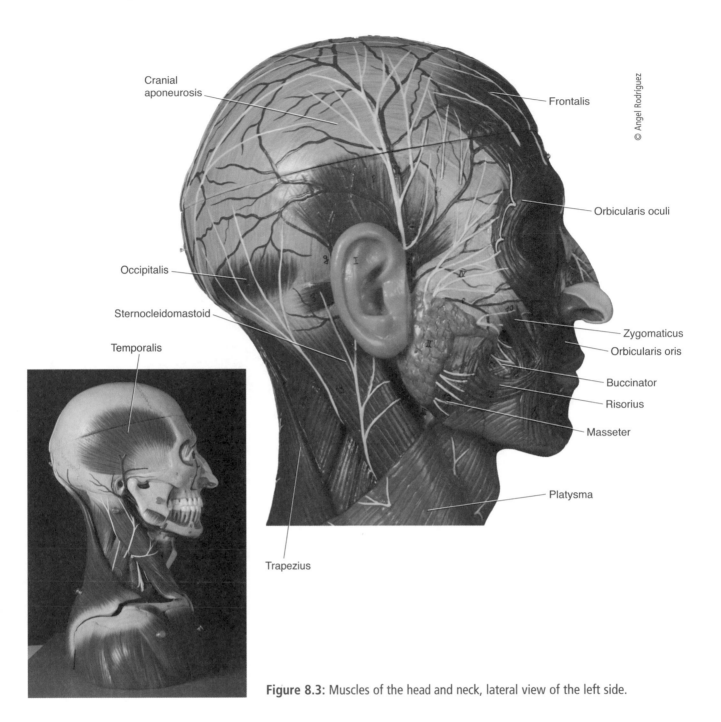

© Angel Rodriguez

Figure 8.3: Muscles of the head and neck, lateral view of the left side.

1. What muscles do you use when you chew?

    _____

2. What muscles turn your head?

    _____

3. What muscles are attached to the temporal bone?

    _____

C. Muscles of the Trunk

The trunk muscles are involved in movements of the upper torso. These muscles move the shoulder, the abdomen, the thoracic wall, and the vertebral column. Most trunk muscles cover large areas of the trunk. Many are wide and flat. Trunk muscles moving the shoulder act upon the humerus, the scapula, or both. Movement of the abdomen that includes rotation and flexion allows you to bend at the waist. These muscles are located on the anterior portion of the trunk. The vertebral column is associated with many muscle groups that extend or flex the column. Muscles that are involved in breathing do so by contracting or expanding the thoracic cavity.

Activity 8.3: Trunk Muscles

1. Identify all the muscles of the trunk listed in Tables 8.4, 8.5, 8.6, and 8.7, by identifying them on models, and charts that are available in your lab.

2. Familiarize yourself with the actions of these muscles. Use Figures 8.4, 8.5, 8.6, and 8.7 as guides.

3. Answer the questions 1-3 in this section.

Table 8.4: Trunk Muscles Moving the Shoulder

Muscle	Description	Origin	Insertion	Action
Pectoralis major	large, fan-shaped muscle covering the upper thorax	clavicle, sternum, cartilages of ribs 2-6	fibers converge to form a short tendon that inserts into the intertubercular groove of the humerus	flexes, adducts, and medially rotates the arm at the shoulder
Deltoid	triangular muscle creating the curvature of the shoulder	acromion and spine of scapula, lateral third of clavicle	deltoid tuberosity of humerus	abduction of the arm
Serratus anterior	large, fan-shaped muscle deep to the scapula with serrated margins	1st to 8th rib	vertebral border of scapula	protracts the shoulder; upward rotation of the scapula
Levator scapulae	between the shoulder and neck; deep to the trapezius	transverse processes of first 4 cervical vertebrae	vertebral border of scapula superior to the spine of the scapula	elevates the scapula
Pectoralis minor	small, thin muscle deep to pectoralis major	3rd, 4th, and 5th rib near costal cartilages	coracoid process of scapula	depresses and protracts the shoulder
Trapezius	large, superior muscle of the back	occipital bone, ligamentum nuchae; spines of C7 and all thoracic vertebrae	acromion and spinous process of scapula; lateral third clavicle	extends the head, rotates and adducts scapula; elevates or depresses the scapula
Latissimus dorsi	broad, flat muscle of the lower back	spinous processes of lower 6 thoracic vertebrae, all lumbar vertebrae, ribs 8-12, and lumbodorsal fascia	intertubercular groove of humerus	extends, adducts, and medially rotates shoulder

Table 8.4: Trunk Muscles Moving the Shoulder (continued)

Muscle	Description	Origin	Insertion	Action
Supraspinatus	deep to trapezius within the supraspinous fossa, a rotator cuff muscle	supraspinous fossa of the scapula	greater tubercle of humerus	abduction at the shoulder
Infraspinatus	deep to trapezius within the infraspinous fossa of scapula; a rotator cuff muscle	infraspinous fossa of the scapula	greater tubercle of humerus	lateral rotation at the shoulder
Teres major	inferior to teres minor and scapula	inferior angle of scapula	intertubercular groove of humerus	extension, adduction, and medial rotation at shoulder
Rhomboids, major and minor	deep to trapezius and medial to the vertebral border of the scapula	spinous processes of C7 and T1 through T5	medial border of scapula	adducts scapula and rotates it downward

Table 8.5: Trunk Muscles Moving the Abdomen

Muscle	Description	Origin	Insertion	Action
Rectus abdominis	medial, segmented superficial muscle of the abdomen	pubic crest and symphysis	xiphoid process and costal cartilages of ribs 5-7	flexes and rotates vertebral column
External oblique	lateral, superficial muscle of the abdomen extending from the pubis to the thoracic cage	ribs 4-12	iliac crest, linea alba (median line), pubic crest and tubercles	flexes and rotates vertebral column
Internal oblique	deep to the external oblique with fibers extending in opposite direction	iliac crest, lumbar fascia	linea alba, pubic crest, costal cartilages of ribs 9-12	flexes and rotates vertebral column
Transverse abdominis	deepest muscle of the abdomen with fibers in horizontal direction	iliac crest, lumbar fascia, inguinal ligament	linea alba and pubic crest	compresses the abdomen

Table 8.6: Muscles Used During Breathing

Muscle	Description	Origin	Insertion	Action
External intercostals	11 pairs extend from rib to rib in oblique downward direction	inferior borders of adjacent rib above	superior border of adjacent rib below	elevates the rib cage
Internal intercostals	11 pairs extend from rib to rib in direction opposite to external intercostals	superior border of rib above	inferior border of rib below	depresses the rib cage
Diaphragm	broad, flat, circular muscle forming the floor of the thoracic cavity	inferior border of rib and sternum, costal cartilages of last 6 ribs and lumbar vertebrae	central tendon (no bone)	flattens to increase the volume of the thoracic cavity

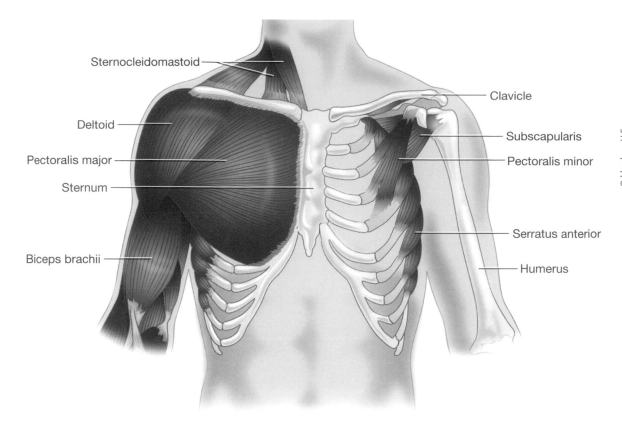

Figure 8.4: Muscles moving the shoulder, anterior view.
The superficial muscles are shown on the right side and deep muscles on the left side.

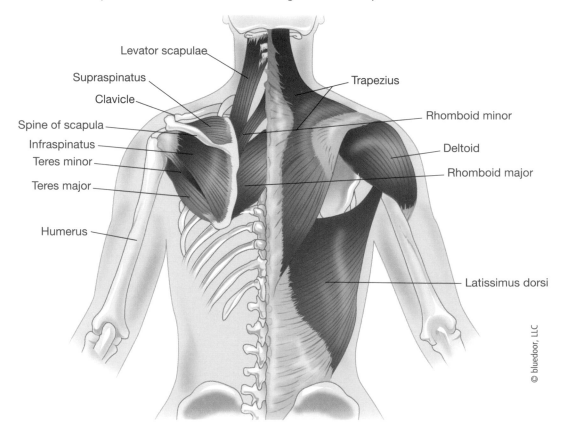

Figure 8.5: Muscles moving the shoulder, posterior view.
Superficial muscles are on the left side, deep muscles on the right side.

1. What muscles of the trunk adduct the arm?

    _____

2. What muscles depress and protract the shoulder?

    _____

3. What muscle flattens to increase the volume during breathing?

    _____

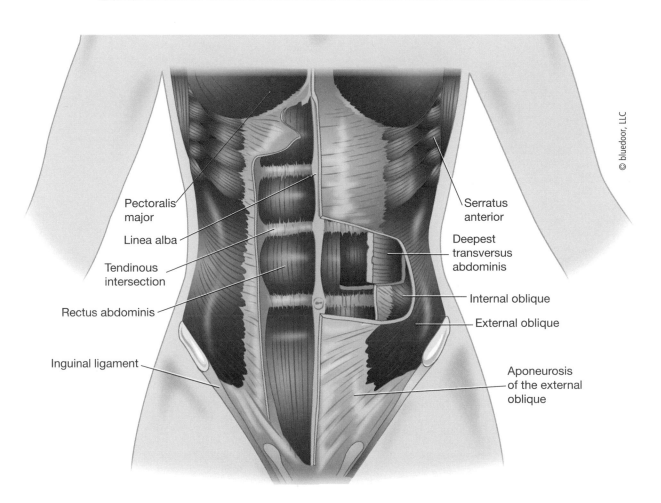

Figure 8.6: Trunk muscles that move the abdomen. The left side shows the aponeurosis removed to reveal the rectus abdominis. The right side shows sections of the external oblique removed.

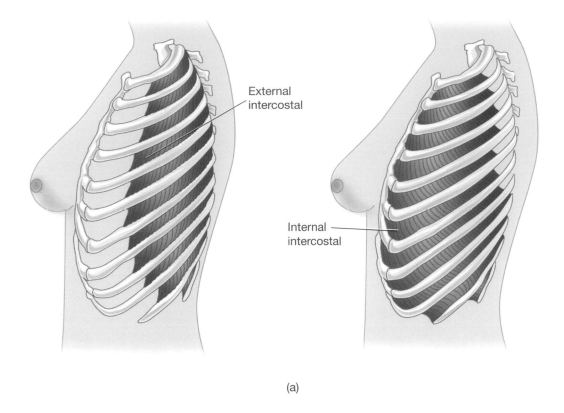

External
intercostal

Internal
intercostal

(a)

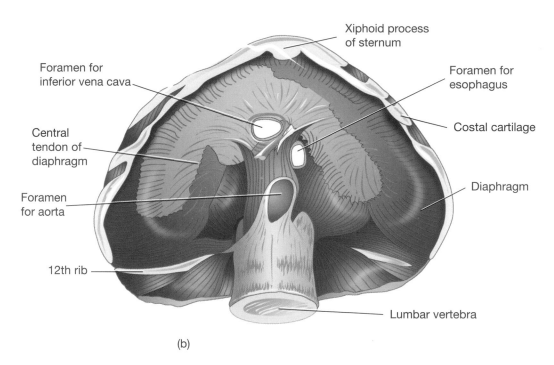

Xiphoid process
of sternum

Foramen for
inferior vena cava

Foramen for
esophagus

Central
tendon of
diaphragm

Costal cartilage

Foramen
for aorta

Diaphragm

12th rib

Lumbar vertebra

(b)

Figure 8.7: Muscles for breathing. (a) The thoracic cage, lateral view, to show the intercostals.
The right diagram is deep. (b) The diaphragm, inferior view.

CHAPTER REVIEW

1. What is the name of the muscle responsible for closing the eyes?
   A. Frontal
   B. Orbicularis oculi
   C. Sternocleidomastoid
   D. Zygomaticus

2. What is the shape of the deltoid muscle?
   A. Long
   B. Pyramidal
   C. Trapezoid
   D. Triangular

3. What is the name of the muscle responsible for closing the jaw?
   A. Buccinator
   B. Masseter
   C. Sternocleidomastoid
   D. Zygomaticus

4. What is the name of the muscle responsible for abduction of the arm?
   A. Pectoralis major
   B. Pectoralis minor
   C. Levator scapulae
   D. Deltoid

5. What is the name of the muscle responsible for smiling?
   A. Frontal
   B. Orbicularis oculi
   C. Sternocleidomastoid
   D. Zygomaticus

6. What is the name of the muscle responsible for extending the head?
   A. Latissimus dorsi
   B. Trapezius
   C. Sternocleidomastoid
   D. Platysma

7. What is the name of the muscle responsible for closing the mouth?
   A. Frontal
   B. Orbicularis oris
   C. Sternocleidomastoid
   D. Zygomaticus

8. The _____ muscle unilaterally turns your head.
   A. Platysma
   B. Levator scapula
   C. Sternocleidomastoid
   D. Serratus anterior

9. What is the name of the muscle responsible for compressing the abdomen?
   A. Rectus abdominis
   B. External oblique
   C. Transversus abdominis
   D. Internal oblique

10. What is the name of the muscle responsible for flattening to increase the volume of the thoracic cavity?
   A. External intercostals
   B. Internal intercostals
   C. Serratus anterior
   D. Diaphragm

Name: _____ Class Time: _____ Class Day: _____

Complete skill checks 1 – 3.

Skill check # 1

1. State five characteristics that are commonly used for naming of muscles.

    _____

2. Contrast the function of the orbicularis oculi and the orbicularis oris.

    _____

3. Why do think the name of the temporalis muscle is appropriate?

    _____

Skill check # 2

1. What is the name of the triangular muscle responsible for abduction of the arm?

    _____

2. Name the large, flat muscle of the back that extends, adducts, and rotates the shoulder.

    _____

3. What muscle is deep to the trapezius, adducts the scapula and rotates it downward?

    _____

Skill check # 3

1. Which three muscles flex and rotate the vertebral column?

    _____

2. Which muscle draws ribs together to depress thorax during breathing?

    _____

3. Which muscles are antagonistic during breathing?

    _____

ALTERNATIVE SKILL CHECKS:

Skill check #1

Be prepared to show your instructor the facial muscles, muscles of mastication, and a muscle that moves the head found in Tables 8.1, 8.2 and 8.3.

Skill check #2

Be prepared to show your instructor the trunk muscles that move the shoulder found in table 8.4.

Skill check #3

Be prepared to show your instructor the **trunk muscles moving the abdomen, and muscles used during breathing** found in table 8.5 and 8.6.

You should show the muscles on models as well as on your own body.

9 Muscles II

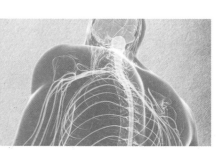

OBJECTIVES:

After completing this laboratory you should be able to perform tasks listed below.

1. Name and state an action of specified muscles of the arm and forearm.
2. Name and state an action of specified muscles of the leg and thigh.
3. Perform experiments to demonstrate muscle physiology.

A. The Muscular System: Arm and Forearm

Activity 9.1: Studying the Muscles of the Arm and Forearm

Study all the muscles of the arm and forearm listed in Tables 9.1 and 9.2 by identifying them on models, and charts that are available in your lab.

Familiarize yourself with the actions of these muscles. Use Figure 9.1 as a helpful guide.

Table 9.1: The Muscles of the Arm and Forearm

Muscle	Description	Origin	Insertion	Action
Deltoid	triangular muscle creating the curve of the shoulder	acromion and spine of scapula, lateral third of clavicle	deltoid tuberosity of humerus	abduction of the arm
Triceps brachii	large muscle of the brachium on the posterior side; it includes three heads of origin: long, lateral, and medial	long head at margin of the glenoid cavity, lateral head at posterior humerus, medial head at distal radial groove of humerus	olecranon process of the ulna	extends the forearm at the elbow
Biceps brachii	large muscle of the brachium on the anterior side	short head at coracoid process, long head travels through the intertubercular groove to the capsule of the shoulder joint	radial tuberosity	flexes the forearm at the elbow and supinates the forearm
Brachioradialis	superficial muscle on the lateral side of the forearm	distal end of humerus	styloid process of radius	flexes the forearm as a synergist
Brachialis	flat muscle deep to the biceps brachii	distal portion of humerus	coronoid process of ulna	flexes the forearm

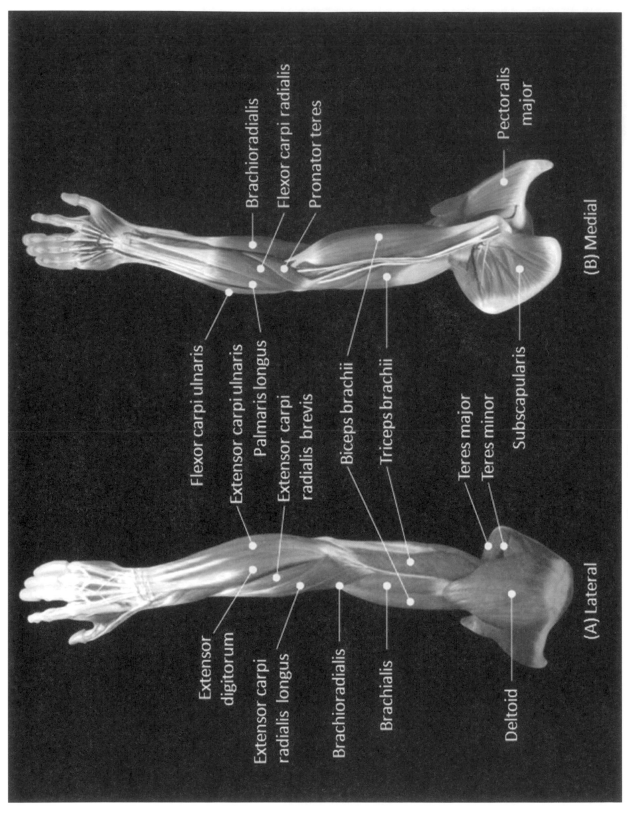

Figure 9.1: Muscles of arm and forearm

Table 9.2: Muscles That Move the Hand and Digits

Muscle	Description	Origin	Insertion	Action
Anterior Side:				
Pronator teres	superficial muscle of forearm between brachioradialis and flexor carpi radialis	medial epicondyle of humerus and coronoid process of ulna	shaft of the radius	pronates the forearm
Flexor carpi radialis	superficial muscle of forearm that partially obscures the pronator teres	medial epicondyle of humerus	base of 2nd and 3rd metacarpals	flexes the hand at the wrist, and abducts the hand at the wrist
Palmaris longus	superficial muscle of forearm medial to flexor carpi radialis	medial epicondyle of humerus	fascia and skin of palm	flexes the hand at the wrist, tenses the skin and fascia of the palm
Flexor carpi ulnaris	superficial muscle of forearm medial to palmaris longus	medial epicondyle of humerus and olecranon process, posterior surface of ulna	base of 5th metacarpal, and pisiform and hamate bones	flexes the hand at the wrist and adducts the hand at the wrist
Posterior Side:				
Extensor digitorum	superficial muscle on the medial side of the forearm	lateral epicondyle of the humerus	by way of four tendons onto distal phalanges of 2nd through 5th digits	extends the digits and hand
Supinator	deep muscle at the posterior side of the proximal forearm	lateral epicondyle of humerus and proximal ulna	proximal end of radius	supinates the forearm at the elbow with the biceps brachii

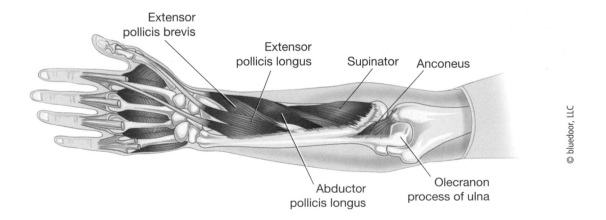

© bluedoor, LLC

Figure 9.2: Superficial and deep muscles of the forearm and hand, posterior view

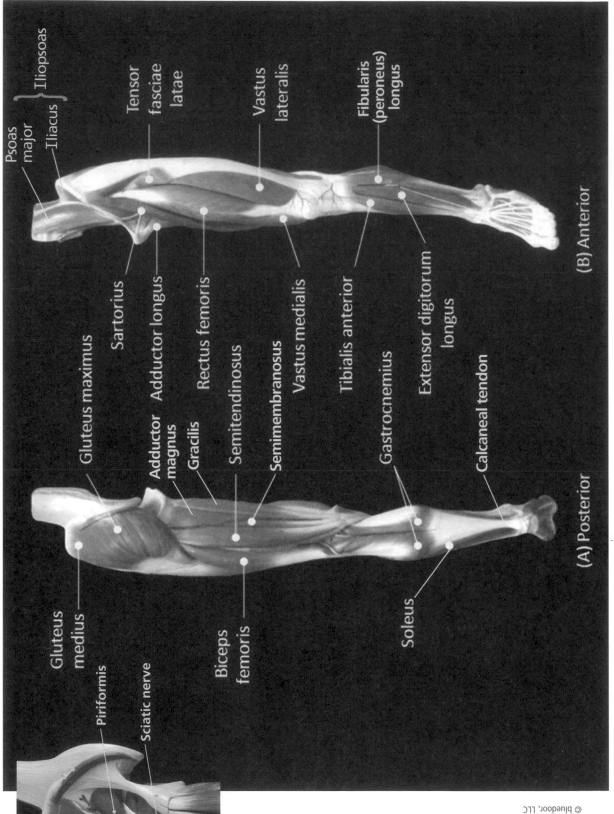

Figure 9.3: Left leg muscles, anterior and posterior view (inset: deep buttock)

B. The Muscular System: Leg and Thigh

Activity 9.2: Studying the Muscles of the Leg and Thigh

Study all the muscles of the leg and thigh listed in Tables 9.3 and 9.4 by identifying them on models, and charts that are available in your lab.

Familiarize yourself with the actions of these muscles. Use Figure 9.3 as a helpful guide.

Table 9.3: Muscles That Move the Thigh at the Hip, the Knee, or Both

Muscle	Description	Origin	Insertion	Action
Iliopsoas	composed of two muscles, the iliacus and psoas major	iliacus at the iliac fossa, psoas major at T12 and lumbar vertebra	lesser trochanter of the femur	flexes the thigh; flexes the trunk; and laterally flexes the vertebral column
Anterior:				
Sartorius	long, thin superficial muscle extending obliquely across the anterior surface of the thigh	anterior superior iliac spine	medial side of proximal tibia	flexes, abducts, and laterally rotates the thigh; flexes the thigh at the knee
Rectus femoris	the anterior muscle of the quadriceps femoris group	anterior inferior iliac spine, superior margin of the acetabulum	tibial tuberosity and patella	extends the knee and flexes the thigh at the hip
Vastus lateralis	the lateral muscle of the quadriceps femoris group	greater trochanter, intertrochanteric line, and linea aspera	tibial tuberosity and patella	extends the knee
Vastus medialis	the medial muscle of the quadriceps femoris group	linea aspera and intertrochanteric line	tibial tuberosity and patella	extends the knee
Vastus intermedius	deep to the rectus femoris	anterior and lateral surface of femur	tibial tuberosity and patella	extends the knee
Tensor fascia latae	lateral side of the thigh between layers of fascia	anterior side of iliac crest and anterior superior iliac spine	iliotibial tract	flexes, abducts, medially rotates the thigh
Posterior Buttocks:				
Gluteus Maximus	the largest muscle of the buttock	posterior iliac crest and sacrum to coccyx	femur	extends thigh
Gluteus Medius	posterior and lateral muscle of the buttock	iliac crest	greater trochanter of the femur	abducts the leg
Piriformis	deep muscle of the buttock	sacrum	greater trochanter of femur	lateral rotation of femur

Table 9.3: Muscles That Move the Thigh at the Hip, the Knee, or Both (continued)

Muscle	Description	Origin	Insertion	Action
Posterior:				
Biceps femoris	large, lateral muscle of the hamstrings group; includes 2 heads of origin, the long head and short head	long head at ischial tuberosity; short head at linea aspera and distal end of femur	head of fibula and lateral condyle of tibia	extends the thigh at the hip; flexes the knee
Semitendinosus	long, narrow muscle of the hamstrings medial to the biceps femoris	ischial tuberosity	medial side of the proximal tibia	extends the thigh at the hip; flexes the knee
Semimembranosus	large, flat muscle of the hamstrings deep to the semitendinosus	ischial tuberosity	medial condyle of the tibia; lateral condyle of the femur	extends the thigh at the hip; flexes the knee
Medial:				
Gracilis	long, narrow superficial muscle of the medial thigh	inferior ramus and body of pubis	medial surface of tibia inferior to medial condyle	adducts the thigh at the hip; flexes and medially rotates the leg
Adductor longus	large superficial muscle of the medial thigh	pubis near pubic symphysis	linea aspera	adducts, medially rotates, and flexes the thigh at the hip
Adductor magnus	large, wide, mostly obscured muscle of the medial thigh	ischial and pubic rami, schial tuberosity	line aspera and adductor tubercle of the femur	adducts, medially rotates, and flexes the thigh at the hip

Table 9.4: Muscles That Move the Foot and Digits

Muscle	Description	Origin	Insertion	Action
Anterior:				
Tibialis anterior	superficial muscle of the anterior side of the leg	lateral condyle and superior shaft of tibia	medial cuneiform and 1st metatarsal	dorsiflexion, inverts foot, supports longitudinal arch
Extensor digitorum longus	lateral to tibialis anterior	lateral condyle of tibia, proximal fibula	middle and distal phalanges of digits 2-5	extension of digits, dorsiflexion

Table 9.4: Muscles That Move the Foot and Digits (continued)

Muscle	Description	Origin	Insertion	Action
Lateral:				
Fibularis (peroneus) longus	superficial muscle on the lateral side of the leg	head and shaft of fibula	1st metatarsal and medial cuneiform	plantar flexion and eversion of the foot
Posterior:				
Gastrocnemius	the large superficial muscle of the calf (posterior leg), with two large bellies and origins	two heads, medial and lateral condyles of the femur	calcaneus by way of the calcaneal tendon	plantar flexes the foot when knee is extended: flexes the leg at the knee
Soleus	flat muscle deep to the gastrocnemius	proximal end of tibia and fibula	calcaneus by way of the calcaneal tendon	plantar flexes the foot
Calcaneal tendon (Achilles tendon)	Tendon at the posterior ankle	Tendon of the posterior calf muscles	calcaneus	Assists the posterior muscles in plantar flexion of the foot

C. Muscle Physiology

Activity 9.3: Muscle Physiology

We're going to do experiments that demonstrate muscle physiology in this part of the lab. Your instructor will give you specific instructions about these experiments.

CHAPTER REVIEW

1. The muscle that is the major abductor of the arm is the _____ muscle.

2. The _____ is composed of two muscles which insert on the lesser trochanter.

3. The _____causes extension of the fingers.

4. What muscle is deep to the gastrocnemius? The _____ muscle.

5. If you wanted to dorsiflex and invert your foot what muscle would you ask to help you do this? _____ muscle.

6. The calcaneal is considered the tendon of the posterior _____ muscles.

7. The word "sartorius" is a Latin word that means pertaining to a tailor. The muscle contracts to rotate your thigh in order to sit in a cross-legged position, which tailors did to alter garments. Name three functions of this muscle.

    1. _____ 2. _____ 3. _____

8. What is the insertion of the rectus femoris? _____and the

    _____

9. Perform the action of flexion of the knee. Palpate the posterior thigh as you do so, and list the muscles responsible for this movement:

    1. _____ 2. _____ 3. _____

10. What muscles only extend the knee? List three muscles:

    1. _____ 2. _____ 3. _____

Name: _____Class Time: _____Class Day: _____

Complete skill checks 1– 3.

Skill check #1

Study the arm model, your instructor will quiz you on the muscles of the arm.

Skill check #2

Study the muscles of the thigh, your instructor will quiz you on the muscles of the thigh.

Skill check #3

Study the muscles of the lower leg, your instructor will quiz you on the muscles and structures of this area.

10 The Nervous System

OBJECTIVES:

After completing this laboratory you should be able to perform tasks listed below.

1. Recognize and state the functions of neurons and neuroglia.
2. Distinguish between the anatomy of a neuron and a nerve.
3. Recognize the major regions of the brain and know their functions.
4. Describe the structural and functional features of the spinal cord.
5. Name and locate the meninges.
6. Dissect a sheep's brain.
7. Identify the olfactory and the optic nerves.
8. Locate the 31 pairs of spinal nerves.
9. Name and locate the major nerve plexuses.

The nervous system has sensory, integrative, and motor functions. Overall, it is concerned with homeostatic regulation of the body. **Neurons** (nerve cells) and **neuroglia** (glial cells) (Figure 10.1) are the cellular components of the system. The neurons transmit electrical signals called nerve impulses or action potentials. In contrast, neuroglial cells provide support, protection, and nourishment for neurons.

Although the nervous system is extremely complex, it has only two principal subdivisions known as the **central nervous system** (**CNS**) and the **peripheral nervous system** (**PNS**). The CNS includes the brain and spinal cord that receive information from sensory receptors, process incoming information, and generate output signals that cause effectors to respond. In contrast, the PNS is composed of ganglia and nerves that transmit impulses to and from the CNS.

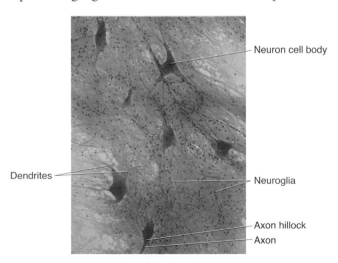

Figure 10.1: Nervous tissue showing neurons and neuroglia

A. NEURONS

Each neuron is composed of a **soma (cell body),** one or more branching **dendrites**, and an **axon** (Figure 10.1). The soma of a neuron contains a nucleus that is surrounded by cytoplasm with numerous other organelles including neurofibrils (cytoskeleton) and **Nissl bodies** (rough endoplasmic reticulum). A cone-shaped **axon hillock** exists at the junction between the axon and the soma of a neuron. Some axons have side branches that are called **axon collaterals**. The axons of myelinated neurons are incompletely wrapped with lipid-rich **myelin sheaths**. A gap known as a **node of Ranvier** exists between each block of myelin and exposes the axon to extracellular fluid. **Axon terminals** exist at the ends of axons and axon collaterals. Electrical impulses (action potentials) received by dendrites of a neuron travel through the cell body, axon, and eventually arrive at the axon terminals where they cause neurotransmitter molecules to be released from the terminal endings of the neuron. These neurotransmitters diffuse across a small space, known as the **synapse**, to stimulate an adjacent neuron, muscle cell, or gland.

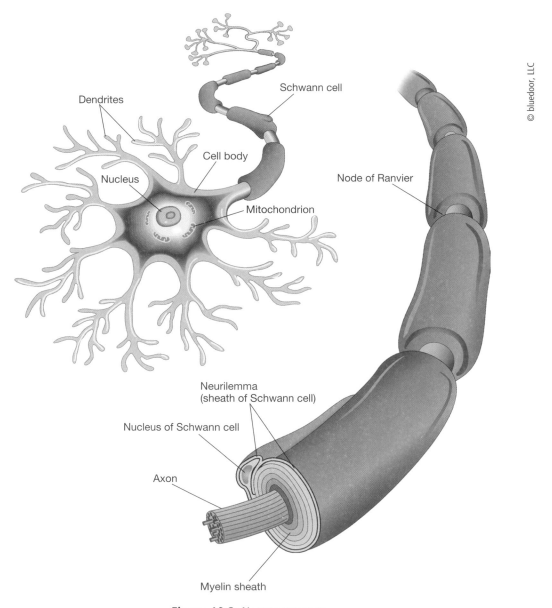

© bluedoor, LLC

Figure 10.2: Neuron structure

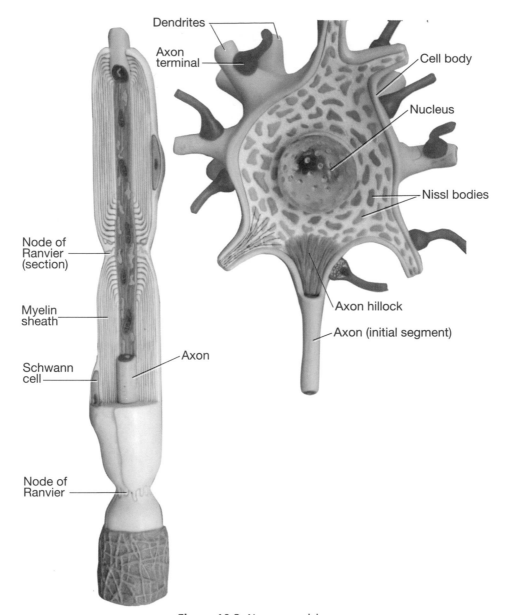

Figure 10.3: Neuron model

Classification of Neurons

Classification of neurons is based on their structural and functional differences. Structurally, neurons are classified as unipolar, bipolar, or multipolar according to the number of structures that branch from a cell body. Functionally, neurons are classified as sensory, association (interneuron), or motor neurons.

Structural Classification of Neurons

Multipolar neurons are located in the CNS. They are motor neurons and interneurons that have numerous dendrites and a single axon. The cell bodies of **multipolar neurons** form the **grey matter** of the CNS and the axons form **tracts** in the **white matter**. In the PNS, axons of multipolar neurons form nerves. **Bipolar neurons** are found in sense organs such as the eye or nose and each of these types of neurons has one axon and one dendrite connected to opposite sides of a cell body. **Unipolar neurons** are located in the PNS and each has a cell body connected to a single process that consists of one axon fused to one dendrite. The cell bodies of **unipolar neurons** form ganglia and the axons form **nerves** in the PNS. Do not confuse a single axon with a nerve. Remember: A nerve contains several bundles of axons (nerve fibers) wrapped in connective tissue.

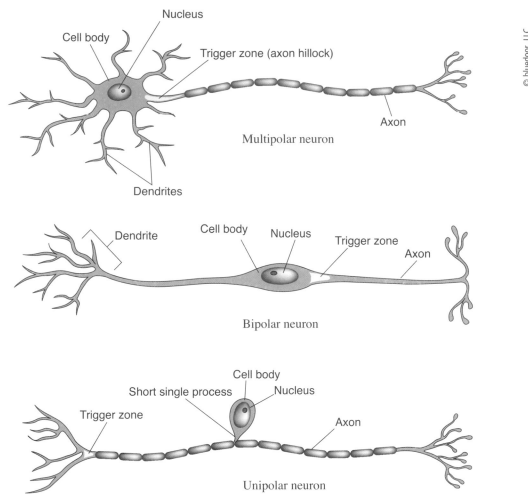

© bluedoor, LLC

Figure 10.4: Structural types of neurons

Functional Classification of Neurons

Sensory (**afferent**) **neurons** transmit electrical impulses from sensory receptors to the CNS. **Interneurons** in the CNS integrate (process) incoming information and generate output. **Motor** (**efferent**) **neurons** transmit impulses away from the CNS to effectors such as muscles or glands.

B. Neuroglia

Neuroglia support and protect neurons. **Astrocytes**, **oligodendrocytes**, **microglia**, and **ependymal cells** are neuroglial cells of the CNS. However, **Schwann cells** and **satellite cells** are located in the PNS. Unlike neurons, neuroglial cells are unable to transmit electrical impulses.

Astrocytes form the blood brain barrier that controls the chemical composition of brain tissue fluid. **Oligodendrocytes** form a protective and insulating myclin sheath around axons of myelinated neurons in the CNS. **Microglia** phagocytize microorganisms, necrotic tissue, and debris in the brain and spinal cord. **Ependymal cells** line the ventricles of the brain and the central canal of the spinal cord. These cells secrete cerebrospinal fluid and they use their cilia to generate a current that helps to circulate the fluid. **Schwann cells** produce the myelin sheath that surrounds myelinated axons of neurons in the PNS. Satellite cells surround and support cell bodies in ganglia. These cells also help to regulate the chemical composition of the environment in the PNS.

Students are required to work in pairs on activities 10.1 to 10.4

Activity 10.1: Observing Motor Neurons and Surrounding Neuroglia

1. Refer to Figures 10.1 and 10.2 and observe a model of a motor neuron.

2. Obtain a prepared slide with giant multipolar neurons.

3. Observe the slide with the high power magnification of a light microscope. Note the small cells surrounding the neurons. These are neuroglial cells.

4. Identify and record the location as well as the function of each structure indicated on Table 10.1.

Table 10.1: Neuron Structures, Their Location, and Function

Structures	Locations	Functions
Axon		
Cell body (soma)		
Dendrites		
Myelin sheath		
Node of Ranvier		

Activity 10.2: Observing Axons of a Teased Nerve

1. Obtain a prepared slide of a teased myelinated nerve that has been sectioned along the longitudinal plane.

2. Observe the nerve with the high power magnification of a light microscope.

3. Identify i) the myelin sheaths that incompletely surround axons of neurons; ii) nodes of Ranvier.

4. In the space provided, draw a representative section of the nerve. Label the axon, myelin sheath, and node of Ranvier.

Your drawing of a representative section of the teased nerve:

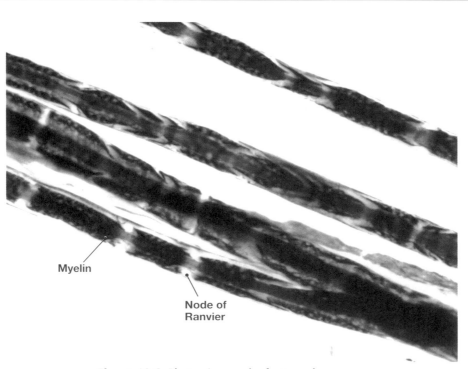

Figure 10.6: Photomicrograph of a teased nerve

C. Brain and Cranial Nerves

The human brain is one of the largest organs of the body. It is divided into four main regions: the **cerebrum**, the **cerebellum**, the **diencephalon**, and the **brain stem** (Figures 10.7a & c). The brain is attached to cranial nerves that carry impulses to and from specific parts of the brain.

Cerebrum

The **cerebrum** (= *big brain*) occupies most of the cranial cavity and it is the most complex part of the brain. A section of the cerebrum reveals an outer layer of gray matter with cell bodies and dendrites known as the **cerebral cortex,** an inner area of **white matter** with axons, and deep **basal ganglia**. A deep groove known as the **longitudinal fissure** divides the cerebrum into right and left **cerebral hemispheres.** Each hemisphere receives and interprets sensory information and generates impulses that initiate motor responses. The cerebral hemispheres also facilitate mental processes such as conscious thought, memory, learning, intelligent behavior, reasoning, and emotional expressions.

The surface of the cerebrum has numerous folds that create ridges called **gyri** and the shallow depressions called **sulci**. The frontal, parietal, temporal, and occipital lobes of the cerebrum that correspond to the bones of the cranium are separated from each other by sulci. The **central sulcus** divides the frontal lobe from the parietal lobes. The **lateral sulcus** divides the parietal lobe from the temporal lobe, and the **parieto-occipital sulcus** divides the parietal and occipital lobes.

Cerebellum

The cerebellum (=*little brain*) has right and left **cerebellar hemispheres** that are connected to each other by the vermis. It is located inferior to the cerebrum within the posterior region of the cranial cavity. The cerebellum regulates posture and equilibrium. In addition, it coordinates skeletal muscle contractions that produce skilled movements. Like the cerebrum, the surface of the cerebellum has numerous gyri and sulci (Figure 10.7a).

Internally, the cerebellum has an outer layer of gray matter known as the cerebellar cortex, and an inner area of white matter. The white matter is organized into narrow branches that resemble those of a tree, earning it the name **arbor vitae** (*arbor* = tree + *vitae* = life). The cerebellum is attached to the rest of the brain by the superior, middle, and inferior cerebellar peduncles.

Diencephalon

The **diencephalon** is located inferior to the cerebrum (Figures 10.7a & c). It contains three main areas: the thalamus, epithalamus, and hypothalamus. The **thalamus** (*thalam* = inner chamber) is composed of gray matter and it is located in the lateral walls of the diencephalon. The **epithalamus** is an area located superior to the thalamus. Specifically, the epithalamus occupies the roof of the diencephalon and includes the cone-shaped **pineal gland (body)** that secretes the hormone melatonin.

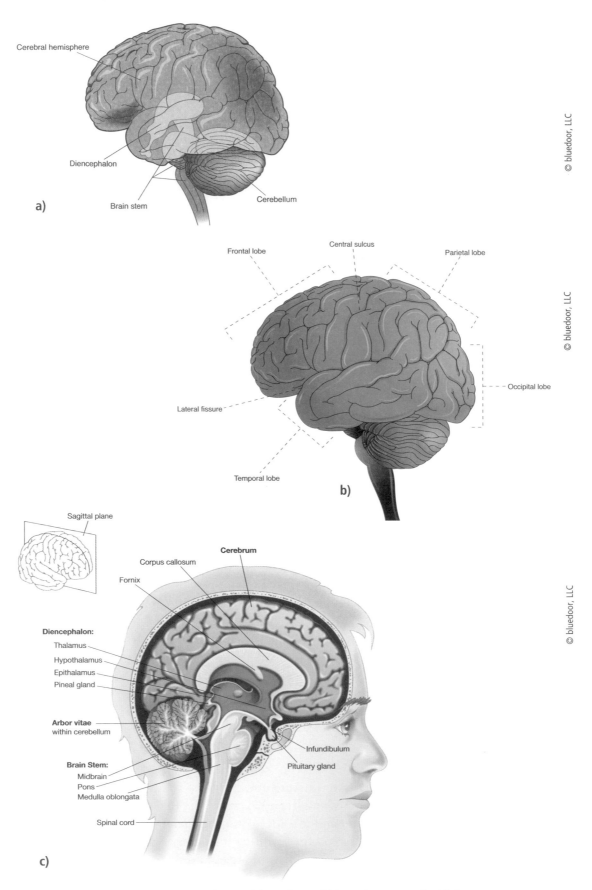

© bluedoor, LLC

Figure 10.7: Human brain: a) lateral view b) lateral view, cerebral lobes
c) midsagittal section

The **hypothalamus** is located inferior to the thalamus and occupies the floor of the diencephalon. Functionally, the thalamus is the brain's primary relay center for sensory fibers
and some motor fibers. The thalamus is also concerned with consciousness, expressions of
emotion, learning, and memory. A narrow stalk called the **infundibulum** and two **mammillary bodies** that serve as relay stations for taste and smell are parts of the hypothalamus.
Anterior to the infundibulum, there is the **optic chiasma** that represents the area where the
optic nerves from each eyeball cross over each other before continuing to the occipital lobe
of the cerebrum. The infundibulum connects the hypothalamus to the pea-shaped **pituitary gland** that is inferior to the brain. The hypothalamus controls the pituitary gland and
integrates activities of the autonomic nervous system (such as heart rate and blood pressure
regulation). It also regulates factors such as emotional and behavioral patterns, circadian
rhythms, body temperature, hunger, thirst, and sleep patterns.

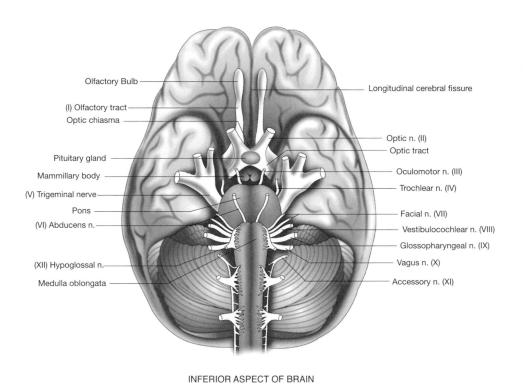

INFERIOR ASPECT OF BRAIN

Figure 10.8: Human brain

Brain Stem

The **brain stem** is the inferior stem-like part of the brain that connects the superior parts of
the brain to the spinal cord. The midbrain, the pons, and the medulla oblongata are three
important components of the brain stem (Figure 10.7c). The **midbrain** is the most superior
part of the brain stem and it is located inferior to the diencephalon. The **cerebral peduncles**
in an anterior position and the **corpora quadrigemina** (*corpora*= bodies; *quadri* = four +
gemina = twin) occupying a posterior location are components of the midbrain. The cerebral peduncles are bundles of myelinated fibers that connect the lower regions of the brain
to the upper regions. The corpora quadrigemina are composed of two **superior colliculi**
(*colliculus* = small mound) and two **inferior colliculi.** The superior colliculi are visual reflex

centers and the inferior colliculi are auditory reflex centers. The **pons** is a widened portion of the brain stem inferior to the midbrain and anterior to the cerebellum that serves as an important relay center of the brain. The pons also assists the medulla to control breathing. The **medulla oblongata** is the most inferior part of the brain and it is connected to the spinal cord. Respiratory and cardiovascular control centers as well as reflex centers concerned with coughing, sneezing, and vomiting are located in the medulla oblongata.

Cranial Nerves

There are 12 pairs of cranial nerves that are visible from the inferior aspect of the human brain (Figure 10.8). Even though the nerves come directly from the brain the cranial nerves belong to the PNS. Unlike the brain, cranial nerves are not a part of the CNS. Each cranial nerve has a name and a number. The cranial nerves derive their names from their function or the structures that they innervate and each cranial nerve is designated by a Roman numeral. Cranial nerves, their location, and their functions are described in Table 10.3.

Activity 10.3: Studying the Brain and Cranial Nerves

1. Examine the external and internal aspects of the model human brain.

2. Identify the parts of the model brain that are labeled on Figures 10.7a, b & c. & 10.8.

3. Use Figure 10.8 to locate cranial nerves I, II, and VIII on the model brain.

SHEEP BRAIN DISSECTION

All students are required to adhere to the following safety rules when handling the preserved brains.

Safety Rules:

- Wear disposable gloves, safety goggles, and a lab coat.
- Dispose of the dissected brains in the biohazard container.
- Wash, disinfect, and dry the dissection equipment.
- Disinfect and dry the table tops with paper towel.
- Wash your hands thoroughly with soap and warm water after this activity.

Activity 10.4: Dissecting a Sheep's Brain

1. Obtain a sheep's brain from the container.
2. Wash the brain thoroughly with tap water to remove preservative.
3. Place the washed brain on a dissecting tray with the brain on its inferior (ventral) side.
4. Examine the superior (dorsal) surface (Figure 10.9). Notice the tough **dura mater (outermost meninx)** that resembles thick plastic.
5. Carefully remove the dura mater. Notice the **falx cerebri** extending into the **longitudinal fissure** and the **tentorium cerebelli** extending into the **transverse fissure**. Deep to the dura mater is the **arachnoid (middle meninx)** that is like a spider's web. The arachnoid will be removed along with the dura mater.
6. Notice the innermost vascular meninx known as the **pia mater** adhering to the surface of the brain.
7. Identify the **gyri** and **sulci** of the cerebrum as well as the cerebellum.
8. Place the brain on its dorsal side and identify the **pons** and **medulla oblongata of the brain stem.** Notice the **spinal cord** that is attached to the medulla.
9. Keep the brain on the dorsal side while you identify the **olfactory bulbs** and **olfactory tracts** of the olfactory nerve (cranial nerve I), the **optic chiasma**, the **cerebral peduncles**, and the **mammillary bodies**.
10. Lift the brain from the dissecting tray and separate the cerebrum from the cerebellum by carefully pulling the cerebellum downward to open the transverse fissure and expose **corpora quadrigemina** in the midbrain (Figure 10.10). You should also be able to observe the **pineal gland** (body).

11. Place the brain on its ventral side in the dissecting tray and press the sharp edge of a large scalpel blade into to the longitudinal fissure. Carefully move the blade back and forth until you cut through the entire brain along the midsagittal plane. Observe the interior of the brain as shown in Figure 10.7c, and identify the **cerebrum**, **corpus callosum**, **fornix, transverse fissure, cerebellum**, **optic chiasma**, **pons**, and **medulla oblongata**.

12. Use a blunt probe to examine the **lateral ventricle**, **third ventricle**, cerebral aqueduct, **fourth ventricle**, that visible in sagittal section of the brain.

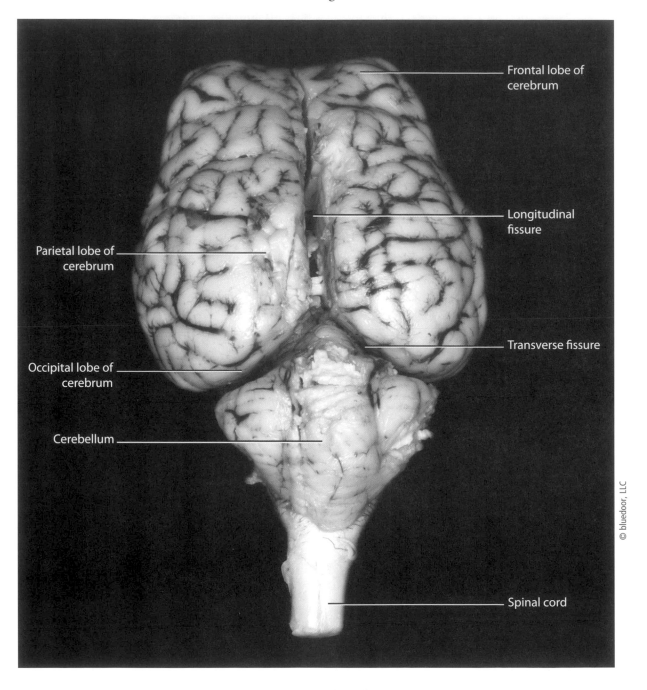

Figure 10.9: Dorsal surface of sheep brain

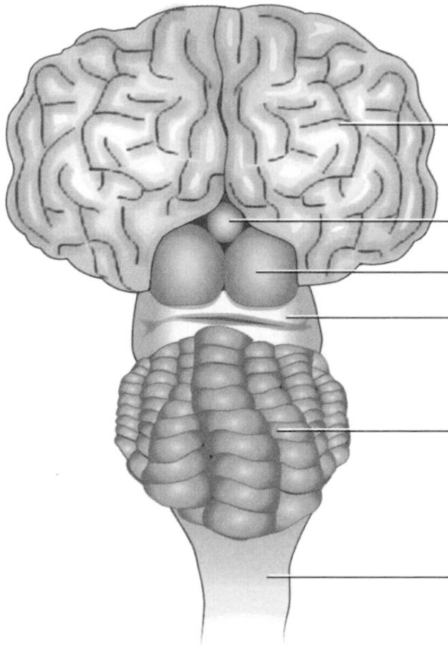

© bluedoor, LLC

Occipital lobe of
cerebral hemisphere

Pineal body

Superior colliculi
of corpora quadrigemina

Inferior colliculi
of corpora quadrigemina

Cerebellum

Spinal cord

Figure 10.10: Sheep brain showing corpora quadrigemina and pineal body

D. The Spinal Cord and Spinal Nerves

External Features of the Spinal Cord

The spinal cord is a delicate cylindrical organ composed of nervous tissue that is concerned with reflex actions and transmission of nerve impulses to and from the brain. The cord extends from the inferior portion of the medulla oblongata in the brain and terminates between vertebrae L1 and L2 (Figure 10.11). In the region of C3 or C4 through T1, there is a **cervical enlargement** or bulge of the spinal cord containing neuron cell bodies (nuclei) that serve the upper limbs. The spinal cord also has a **lumbar enlargement or** bulge between T9 through T12 that contains nuclei serving the lower limbs. The terminal portion of the cord is cone-shaped and called the **conus medullaris**. Associated with the conus medullaris is the **cauda equina** (*cauda* = tail; *equina* = horse) consisting of nerves that arise from the inferior portion of the spinal cord and extend downward to resemble a horseís tail.

Protection of the delicate spinal cord is achieved by the vertebral column, meninges (sing. meninx), cerebrospinal fluid, and fat. The three protective meninges that surround the brain also surround the spinal cord (Figure 10.12). Like the situation with the brain, the **dura mater** is the outermost meninx and the middle meninx is the **arachnoid.** The **pia mater** is the innermost meninx that adheres to the surface of the spinal cord and forms folds called denticulate ligaments that hold the cord in place within the vertebral foramina of the protective vertebral column. Beyond the conus medullaris, the pia mater forms fibrous extensions called the **filum terminale** that terminates in the vicinity of S2 and connects the spinal cord to the coccyx. A fat-filled **epidural space** surrounds the dura mater and serves as a shock absorber. Protective cerebrospinal fluid that flows through the brain transporting oxygen, nutrients, and other materials also flows through the central canal of the spinal cord.

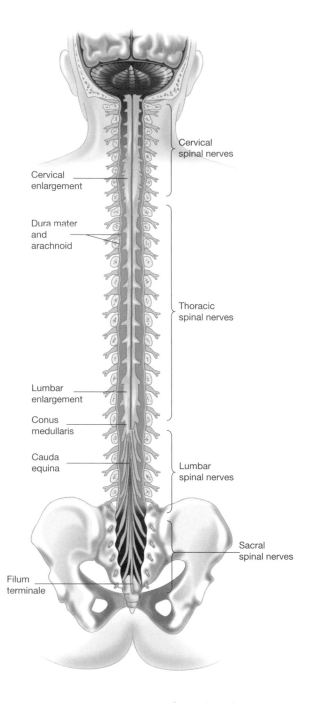

Cervical
spinal nerves

Cervical
enlargement

Dura mater
and
arachnoid

Thoracic
spinal nerves

Lumbar
enlargement

Conus
medullaris

Cauda
equina

Lumbar
spinal nerves

Sacral
spinal nerves

Filum
terminale

Figure 10.11: Posterior view of spinal cord

Internal Features of the Spinal Cord

Internally, the spinal cord has central **gray matter** that processes and integrates incoming nerve impulses and peripheral **white matter** that transmits nerve impulses to and from the brain. The **gray matter is composed** of neuron cell bodies with their associated dendrites and it surrounds a **central canal** containing cerebrospinal fluid. A landmark feature of a spinal cord's gray matter is its shape which looks like a butterfly or letter "H." This shape exists because of the **anterior (ventral) horns, posterior (dorsal) horns**, **lateral horns** and a **gray commissure** that connects the right and left sides of the gray matter. The white matter consists of **tracts** that are composed of myelinated axons of neurons (nerve fibers).

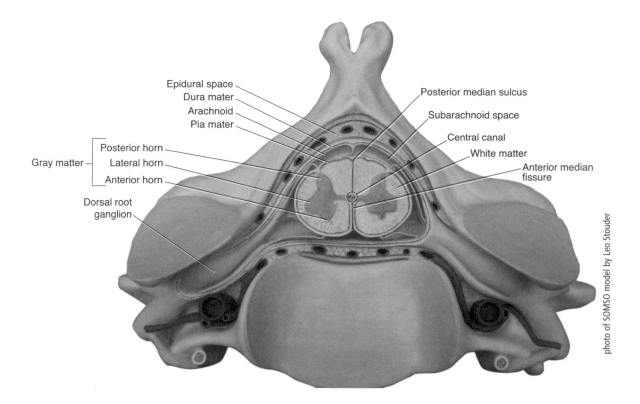

Gray matter
- Posterior horn
- Lateral horn
- Anterior horn

Epidural space
Dura mater
Arachnoid
Pia mater

Dorsal root ganglion

Posterior median sulcus
Subarachnoid space
Central canal
White matter
Anterior median fissure

photo of SOMSO model by Leo Stouder

Figure 10.12: Transverse section of spinal cord and a cervical vertebra

Spinal Nerves

There are 31 pairs of spinal nerves that arise from the lateral aspect of the spinal cord, pass through intervertebral foramina, and terminate in the regions of the body that they innervate. Spinal nerves are organs of the peripheral nervous system that transmit nerve impulses to and from the spinal cord of the central nervous system. Each spinal nerve consists of **fasicles** or bundles of axons of neurons (nerve fibers) surrounded by three protective connective tissue layers. The **epineurium** (*epi* = upon + *neurium* = pertaining to a nerve) surrounds the whole nerve. The **perineurium** (*peri* = around) surrounds each bundle of fibers (fascicle). The **endoneurium** (*endo* = within) surrounds each axon.

The spinal nerves are classified as mixed nerves because they contain axons of sensory and motor neurons. **Posterior (dorsal) roots** of spinal nerves contain sensory fibers and **anterior (ventral) roots** contain motor fibers. The **posterior roots** transmit impulses from sensory receptors to the spinal cord and the **anterior roots** transmit impulses from the spinal cord to effectors. A **posterior (dorsal) root ganglion** containing cell bodies of sensory neurons is associated with the posterior root of each spinal nerve. The anterior roots of spinal nerves in four regions of the body branch as well as anastomose (merge) repeatedly to form cervical, brachial, lumbar, and sacral nerve **plexuses** (networks) on the left and right sides of the vertebral column (Figure 10.13).

The **cervical plexus** is formed from the anterior rami (branches) of spinal nerves C1-C5 and it innervates muscles of the shoulder and neck. The **phrenic nerves** that innervate the diaphragm and help to control breathing arise from spinal nerves C3, C4, and C5. The **brachial plexus** is formed from the anterior rami of C5-T1. **Axillary nerves** arising from brachial plexuses innervate the muscles and skin of the shoulder. The **radial nerves** also arise from the brachial plexuses and they extend down the posterolateral sides of the arms and forearms to innervate the muscles and skin along their path. The **median nerves** passes down the anteromedial side of the arms. The **lumbar plexus** arises from the anterior rami of L1-L4 and some of its nerves serve the lower abdominopelvic region and the anterior thigh. The femoral nerves are large nerves that arise from the lumbar plexuses and they innervate the anterior thigh muscles. The **sacral plexus** is formed from the anterior rami of L4-S4 and its nerves serve the gluteal region, the perineal region, and most regions of the lower limbs. The **sciatic nerve** arises from the sacral plexus, extends through the sciatic notch and continues down the posterior thigh to serve the flexor muscles and skin that exist along its path.

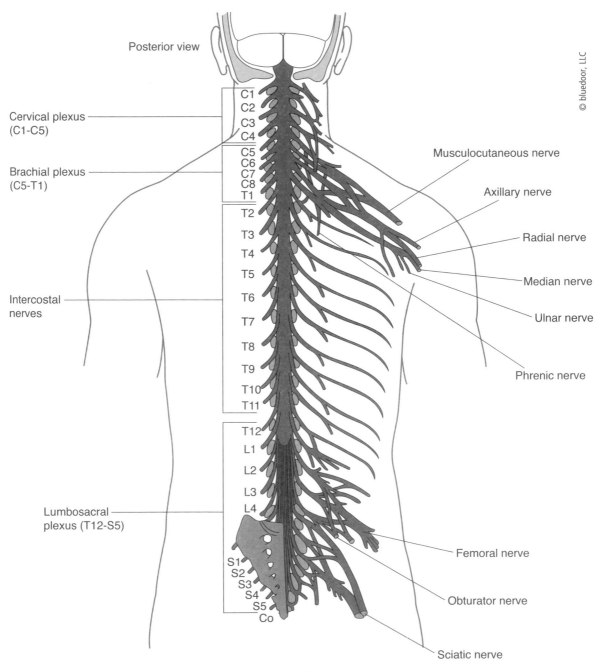

© bluedoor, LLC

Figure 10.13: Posterior view of spinal cord and spinal nerves

Activity 10.5: Observing Spinal Cord and Spinal Nerves

1. Refer to Figure 10.11 and identify the **cervical plexus, cervical enlargement, thoracic nerves, lumbar enlargement, lumbar plexus, sacral plexus, conus medullaris, cauda equinae**, and the **filum terminale** on a model showing the posterior view of the spinal cord. Refer to Figure 10.12 and identify the **anterior gray horns, posterior gray horns, lateral gray horns, gray commissure, central canal, anterior median fissure, posterior median sulcus, posterior white columns, posterior (dorsal) root of spinal nerve, posterior (dorsal) root ganglion, anterior (ventral) root of spinal nerve, pia mater, subarachnoid space, arachnoid, dura mater**, and the **epidural space** on a model showing the transverse section of the spinal cord.

2. Obtain a prepared slide with the transverse section of the spinal cord.

3. Observe the slide with the low power magnification of a light microscope and identify the **anterior gray horns, posterior gray horns, lateral gray horns**, and the **white columns**.

CHAPTER REVIEW

1. The two principal divisions of the nervous system are the _____.
   A. central and the somatic nervous systems
   B. central and the peripheral nervous systems
   C. peripheral and the somatic nervous systems
   D. peripheral and the autonomic nervous systems
2. Nerves are composed of _____.
   A. dendrites
   B. bundles of axons
   C. cell bodies and axons of neurons
   D. clusters of cell bodies of neurons

3. The part of the brain that connects with the pituitary gland is the _____.
   A. thalamus
   B. hypothalamus
   C. medulla oblongata
   D. pons

4. Corpora quadrigemina are components of the _____.
   A. cerebellum
   B. cerebrum
   C. pons
   D. midbrain

5. Epidural space in the spinal column is occupied by _____.
   A. protein filaments
   B. myelin
   C. fat
   D. cartilage

6. The innermost meninx of the brain and spinal cord is the _____.
   A. dura mater
   B. pia mater
   C. arachnoid
   D. gyrus

7. Ventral rami of the spinal nerves form nerve plexuses in all regions of the body except the _____.
   - A. cervical region
   - B. thoracic region
   - C. brachial region
   - D. lumbar region

8. Motor neurons transmit impulses from _____.
   - A. effectors to the central nervous system
   - B. receptors to the central nervous system
   - C. the central nervous system to effectors
   - D. the central nervous system to receptors

9. Ganglia are clusters of _____.
   - A. cell bodies in the central nervous system
   - B. cell bodies in the peripheral nervous system
   - C. rough endoplasmic reticulum in a cell body
   - D. microtubles involved with transport in axons

10. Which one of the following is concerned with processing and integration of incoming nerve impulses?
   - A. Gray matter
   - B. White matter
   - C. Meninges
   - D. Posterior root ganglia

Name: _____ Class Time: _____ Class Day: _____

Complete skill checks 1 – 3.

Skill check #1

State the functions of each of the following structures:

1. Dendrites

    _____

2. Axons

    _____

3. Myelin sheaths

    _____

Skill check #2

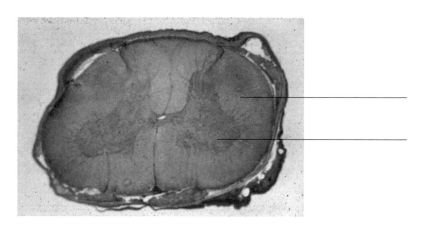

Figure 10.14: Organ "A"

1. Identify organ "A" shown in Figure 10.14

    _____

2. Label the outer and inner regions of organ "A" that are indicated.

Skill check #3

Name each of the following structures indicated on Figure 10.15.

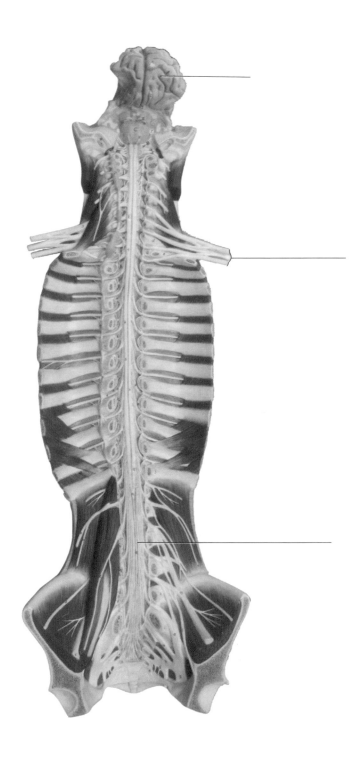

Figure 10.15: Spinal cord and spinal nerves model

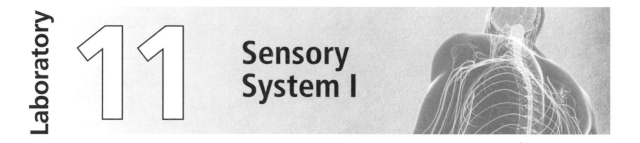

Sensory System I

OBJECTIVES:

After completing this laboratory you should be able to perform tasks listed below.

1. Perform physiological experiments to demonstrate selected reflexes.
2. Identify cutaneous receptors.
3. Perform exercises investigating the physiology of cutaneous receptors such as sensations of touch, heat and cold and two-point threshold.
4. Perform exercises related to smell and taste.
5. Identify the structures of the ear and describe their functions.
6. Perform physiological exercises related to hearing.

A. Reflexes

A rapid response for the purpose of maintaining homeostasis is called a reflex. It is an involuntary action triggered by the central nervous system (CNS). Reflexes provide protection in response to a stimulus in order to avoid or minimize injury to the body. Reflexes can be somatic or autonomic (visceral). A reflex resulting in the contraction of skeletal muscle is known as a somatic reflex. An autonomic reflex causes the contraction of cardiac muscle or smooth muscle or secretion of glands.

Reflexes occur after nerve impulses travel through a reflex arc involving five components (Figure 11.1):

1. **Sensory receptor**: This is a receptor that generates an action potential (low voltage).

2. **Sensory neuron**: This neuron conducts the action potential to the CNS and terminates at a synapse in the spinal cord or in the brain stem.

3. **Integration center**: This center exists within the gray matter of the CNS and it allows the action potential to be transmitted from a sensory to a motor neuron.

4. **Motor neuron**: The action potential travels from the integration center through a motor neuron to an effector (muscle or gland).

5. **Effector**: It is stimulated by the action potential to perform work. Effectors may be a skeletal muscle fiber as in a somatic reflex, cardiac muscle, smooth muscle, or gland as in a visceral reflex.

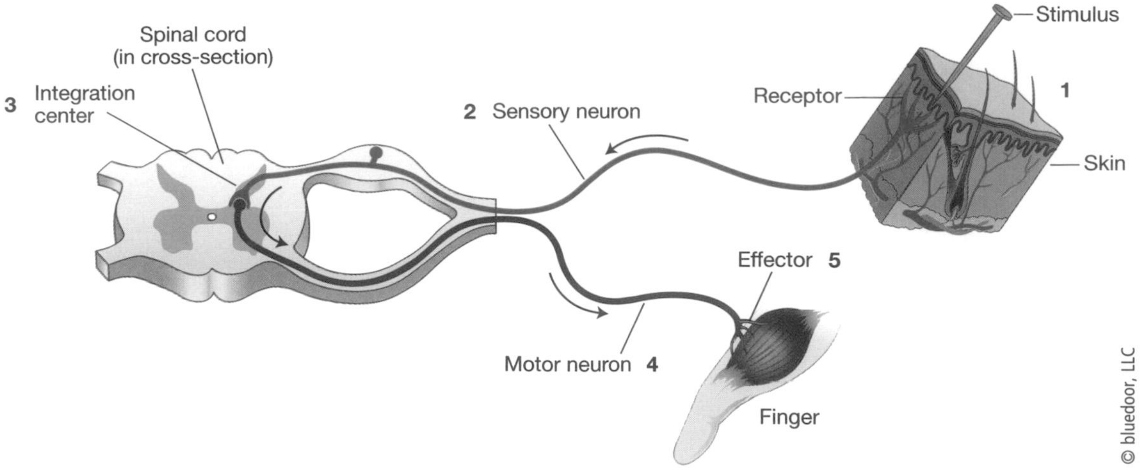

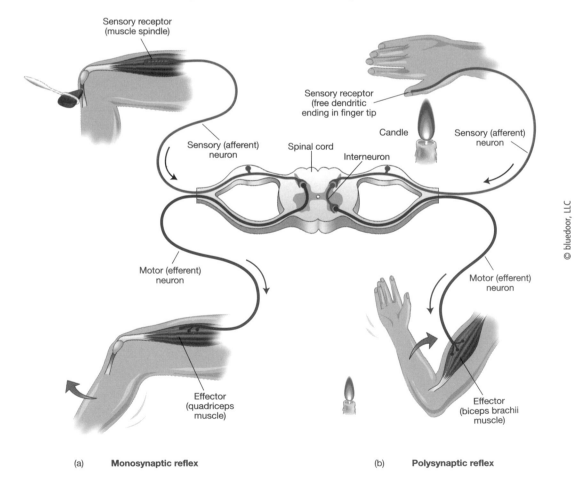

Figure 11.1: A simple reflex arc. The numbers correspond to the sequences in the text.

The reflex arc illustrated above is **monosynaptic** and consists of just two neurons. Most reflexes of the body are more complex or **polysynaptic**, involving several neurons (Figure 11.2). Testing for reflexes is a procedure performed to determine if a patient has suffered peripheral nerve problems or spinal cord and brain damage or disease.

(a)   **Monosynaptic reflex**   (b)   **Polysynaptic reflex**

Figure 11.2: Monosynaptic and polysynaptic reflexes.
(a) Monosynaptic reflex uses two neurons, such as the patellar reflex.
(b) A polysynaptic reflex uses more than two neurons, such as the biceps reflex.

Activity 11.1: Observing Somatic Reflexes

In this activity you will observe two somatic reflexes: the patellar and the biceps reflex.

1. **Patellar reflex**. When the patellar tendon is stretched, the response is a rapid extension of the leg at the knee. The reflex arc is illustrated in Figure 11.2a.

   a. Ask your partner to sit on a lab stool with one leg dangling free of contact from the stool or the floor. Palpate the tibial tuberosity and the patella. The patellar tendon is located between the two structures and serves as the insertion of the quadriceps femoris muscle. You will know that you have found the patellar tendon if you can sense motion once the partner tenses the quadriceps muscles.

   b. Firmly but gently, tap the patellar tendon using the tapered end of a rubber-tipped reflex hammer. Does the reflex occur? _____

   c. If the reflex does not occur, repeat the test. However, this time distract your partner's attention by asking him or her to describe the most recent meal while you test for the reflex. Do you observe any difference in the response with the distraction? _____

   d. If you observe any difference, suggest an explanation. _____

   _____

   _____

2. **Biceps reflex**. A sudden stretch of the biceps tendon will elicit the biceps reflex which is the rapid contraction of the biceps brachii muscle.

   a. With your lab partner still sitting, place his or her hand on the thigh, palm up and relaxed. With the biceps flexed, palpate the biceps tendon that is located in the antecubital fossa (elbow crease).

   b. Place your thumb over the tendon and ask your partner to keep the arm relaxed. Firmly but gently, tap on your thumb with the tapered end of the reflex hammer. Does the biceps reflex occur? _____

   _____

   c. Repeat the procedure on the biceps tendon of the opposite arm. How many neurons are involved in this reflex?

   _____

B. Sensory Receptors

A sensory receptor is a sensory nerve ending or receptor cell that detects a stimulus in the internal or external environment. Each type of sensory receptor has a specific function. For example, **free nerve endings** detect extreme pressure or injury that the brain interprets as pain. Free nerve endings also detect slight touch that results in a tickle sensation or itch. Touch and pressure are also detected by structural receptors called **encapsulated nerve endings.** The dendrites of these receptors are enclosed by a capsule of connective tissue.

Nerve endings that are found in the skin are referred to as cutaneous receptors (Figure 11.3). They include Merkel discs, nociceptors, Meissner's corpuscles and Pacinian corpuscles. The **Merkel discs** are mechanoreceptors that detect light touch. Specifically, they are free nerve endings in the basal layer of the epidermis. The **Nociceptors** are free nerve endings that detect painful mechanical stimuli, extreme heat or cold, and chemical stimuli that can cause tissue damage. The **Meissner's corpuscles** or tactile corpuscles and **Pacinian corpuscles** are encapsulated nerve endings. Meissners corpuscles are located in the dermal papillae of hairless skin and they detect light touch. Pacinian corpuscles are found deep within the dermis and they detect pressure and heavy touch.

Receptors that are responsible for sensing body position are called **proprioceptors**, and are found within skeletal muscles (Figure 11.4). There are two types of proprioceptors: muscle spindles and Golgi tendon organs. The **muscle spindles** contain minute extensions of dendrites that coil within the belly of a muscle and primarily detect changes in the length of skeletal muscle cells. The **Golgi tendon organs** are composed of dendrites within the tendons in proximity to the muscle-tendon area. When movement in the body occurs the muscles or tendons change in length. This stretching is interpreted by the cerebellum as change in body position and movement.

Activity 11.2: Observing Sensory Receptors

1. Observe models of the skin and identify the cutaneous receptors that are illustrated in Figure 11.3.

2. Describe the location of Merkel discs in the skin.

_____

_____

_____

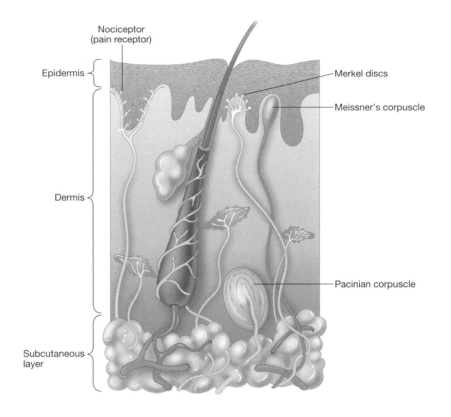

© bluedoor, LLC

Figure 11.3: Cutaneous receptors

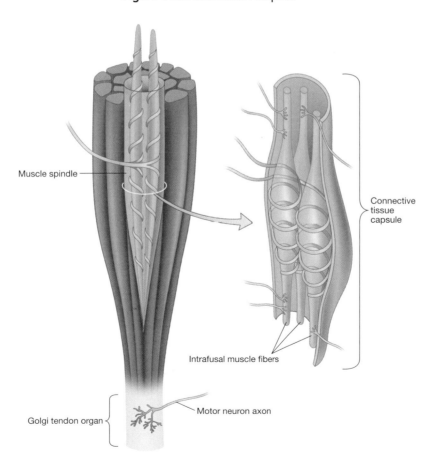

© bluedoor, LLC

Figure 11.4: Proprioceptors in skeletal muscle

C. General Senses

The general senses include touch, pain, heat and cold. Sensory receptors receive stimuli from the environment and convert them into action potentials during a process known as transduction. All action potentials are identical. So, the brain interprets the action potentials based on the area of the sensory cortex that is stimulated. The path through which nerve impulses travel enables the brain to distinguish one of four sensations recognized as touch, pain, heat and cold.

Sensory receptors are located in specific regions of the skin. The fingertips and anterior side of the forearm require special sensitivity and have concentrated clusters of touch receptors. The most abundant receptors, the nociceptors or pain receptors are concentrated in areas of the body in greatest need of protection from injury like internal organs. Some areas of the skin, like your elbow, have little or no sensation because very few receptors are present.

Activity 11.3: The Two-Point Discrimination Test

The two-point discrimination test examines the distribution of cutaneous receptors (Figure 11.5). Using a set of calipers and a metric ruler, you will measure the distance between two light touch receptors by touching your partner's skin simultaneously at two points.

1. Use the points of calipers that are completely closed (together) to make contact with your partner's skin on the palm of the hand.

2. Gradually increase the distance between the caliper arms and repeat step #1 until your partner experiences light touch.

3. Once your partner first identifies the sense of light touch, open the caliper arms slightly and continue to make additional contacts. Continue opening the caliper arms by small increments and keep testing until your partner feels two points of contact. This area represents the minimal distance that two points can be felt or the **two-point threshold**. Use a metric ruler to measure this distance and record it in the data table below. **Remember to touch the two points at exactly the same time.**

4. Repeat the two-point testing procedure on the back of the hand, the fingertips, the anterior side of the forearm, the posterior side of the forearm, and the face.

5. Review the data and write your conclusion about the distribution of touch receptors in the body.

Data Table: Two-Point Threshold Test

Body area tested	Two-point threshold (mm)
Palm of the hand	
Back of the hand	
Fingertip	
Anterior side of a forearm	
Posterior side of a forearm	
Face	

Conclusion: _____

_____

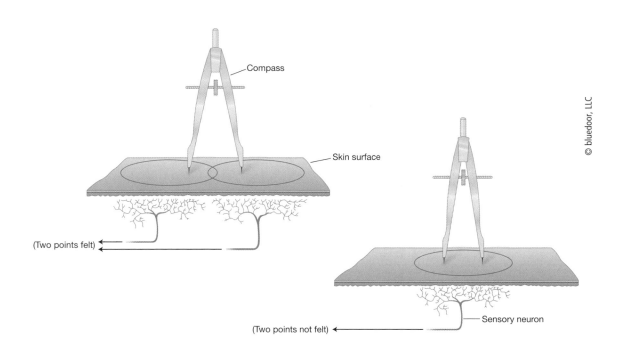

Compass

Skin surface

(Two points felt)

(Two points not felt)

Sensory neuron

© bluedoor, LLC

Figure 11.5: The two-point discrimination test.
Note: When two points can be felt, two sensory receptors are being stimulated.

D. Special Senses

There are five special senses of the human body. These senses are hearing, smell, taste, and vision. In this lab we will explore the special senses of hearing, balance or equilibrium, smell, and taste by performing a series of laboratory activities.

a) Anatomy of the Ear

The ear is a complex organ that houses the sensory receptors for hearing and equilibrium. It is divided into three parts: the outer (external) ear, the middle ear, and the inner ear (Figure 11.6). The outer ear collects and funnels sound waves, which are converted to mechanical vibrations by the tympanic membrane (*tympan* = drum) or eardrum. The middle ear is an air-filled cavity with 3 ossicles that transmit vibrations from the tympanic membrane to the oval window.

The inner ear consists of a labyrinth (maze) embedded within the temporal bone containing the mechanoreceptors that trigger both hearing and equilibrium.

The **outer ear** or external ear is composed of the parts described below:

Auricle: also called the pinna is the external appendage of the ear composed of elastic cartilage and covered with skin. Its function is to direct sound waves into the ear canal. The outer rim of the ear is called the helix and the inferior portion to the opening is called the lobule.

External auditory canal: also called the external auditory meatus (*meatus* = opening) is the opening that connects the external ear with the middle ear. It is located in the temporal bone and it is about 2.5 cm long. The canal is lined with skin that contains ceruminous or wax-secreting glands.

Tympanic (*tympan* = drum) membrane: also called the eardrum is a thin membrane made of tissue similar to skin. It separates the outer ear and middle ear and converts sound into mechanical vibrations that it transfers to the middle ear.

The **middle ear** is composed of the parts described below:

Auditory ossicles: consist of three small bones the **malleus** (hammer), **incus** (anvil), and the **stapes** (stirrup) within the tympanic cavity. These bones articulate to form a small lever system, which serve to amplify and transmit mechanical vibrations from the tympanic membrane (Figure 11.7).

Auditory tube: it is a narrow flatten tube connecting the middle ear and the pharynx. It is also known as the Eustachian or pharyngotympanic tube. The tube is usually closed, but yawning and swallowing opens it up to equalize middle ear and atmosphere pressure.

Oval window: named because of its shape, the oval window is a small membrane-covered opening that attaches the base of the stapes to the inner ear.

Round window: named because of its shape, the round window is a small membrane-covered opening situated below and a little behind oval window. It transmits vibrations and stimulates the fluid of the cochlea in the inner ear.

The **inner ear** is composed of bony and membranous labyrinths. Both labyrinths form three regions: the semicircular canals, the vestibule and the cochlea.

Bony labyrinth: consists of a system of fluid passages in the inner ear lined with bone. The extracellular fluid is called perilymph.

Membranous labyrinth: consists of a membrane-lined canal enclosed within the bony labyrinth. It is filled with a viscous fluid called endolymph. Both labyrinths form three regions: the semicircular canals, the vestibule, and the cochlea.

Semicircular canals: three half circles or semicircles, the interior consists of a membranous labyrinth filled with perilymph. Each loop has widened ends called ampullae, which contain sensory receptors involved with equilibrium.

Vestibule: situated in the middle of the bony labrinth. It contains two chambers bound by the membranous labyrinth. The **saccule** is the anterior chamber and the **utricle** is the posterior chamber. The sensory receptors located in these chambers detect changes in head position and the force of gravity that allow the brain to distinguish the positions of the body.

Cochlea: resembling a snail's shell is the third chamber and contains the sensory receptors called hair cells for hearing. It contains a membranous labyrinth that encloses the cochlear duct and it is connected to the saccule. Hair cells of the cochlea are located within the **spiral organ of Corti**.

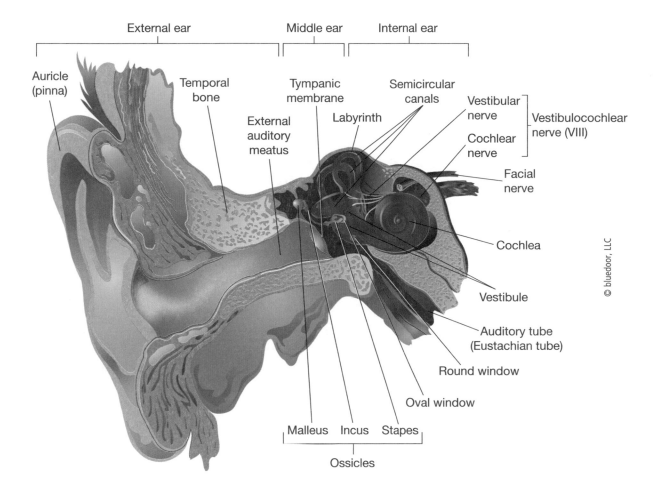

Figure 11.6: Anatomy of the ear.

Activity 11.4: Studying the Anatomy of the Ear

1. Study models and charts of the ear that are available in the lab.

2. Refer to Figure 11.6 and label Figures 11.7 and 11.8.

1. Identify the following structures:

External ear	Middle ear	Inner ear
auricle	incus	vestibule
external auditory meatus	malleus	cochlea
tympanic membrane	stapes	cochlear duct
	auditory (Eustachian) tube	semicircular canals
	oval window	vestibulocochlear nerve (CN-VIII)
	round window	

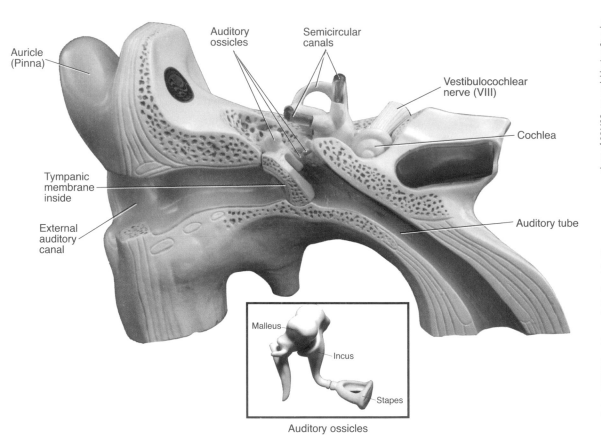

Figure 11.7: Anatomy of the ear (inset: auditory ossicles)

2. Review the anatomy of the ear by naming the structures indicated on the figure
    below.

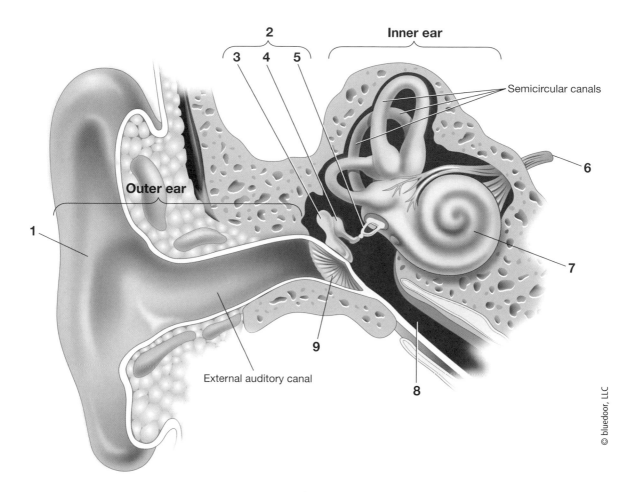

Figure 11.8: Anatomy of the ear

1. _____   6. _____

2. _____   7. _____

3. _____   8. _____

4. _____   9. _____

5. _____

Activity 11.5: Performing the Weber Test

Loss of hearing may be conductive and/or neural. Conductive hearing loss is due to a failure to conduct sound waves to the inner ear. Neural hearing loss occurs due to nerve damage such as damage to the vestibulocochlear nerve (CN-VIII). In this activity, you will perform the Weber test that examines the ability of the ear to conduct sound waves.

1. Working with a partner, obtain a tuning fork and instruct your partner to sit with the head erect and facing forward.

2. Holding the tuning fork by the handle, strike it on the palm of your hand, and place the handle at the top of his or her skull.

3. Ask your partner, "Do you hear, or feel the vibration, in your left ear, your right ear or in the middle?"

4. Holding the tuning fork by the handle, strike it on the palm of your hand, and place the handle at the top of his or her skull and have your partner put one hand over one ear so that the ear canal is closed. Find out if your partner can hear the sound in the closed ear. This is called lateralization.

Which one of the following statements best describes your results?

a. Equal loudness in both ears – normal hearing or equal hearing loss in both ears

b. Left ear sound is louder – (sound lateralized to the left) conduction deafness in left ear or nerve deafness in right ear.

c. Right ear sound is louder – (sound lateralized to the right) conduction deafness in right ear or nerve deafness in left ear.

b) The Nose and Olfaction

The sense of smell or olfaction is detected by chemoreceptors called olfactory cells in the olfactory epithelium of the nose (Figure 11.9). The olfactory cells are bipolar neurons and they are surrounded by supporting cells. Their dendrites are embedded in the nasal mucosa and they form olfactory hairs that are the actual receptors of dissolved chemicals.

The axons of the olfactory cells form the olfactory nerves. These nerves pass through foramina in the cribriform plate of the ethmoid bone to synapse with neurons in the olfactory bulb. The action potentials that are generated by olfactory cells travel to the temporal lobe of the cerebral cortex.

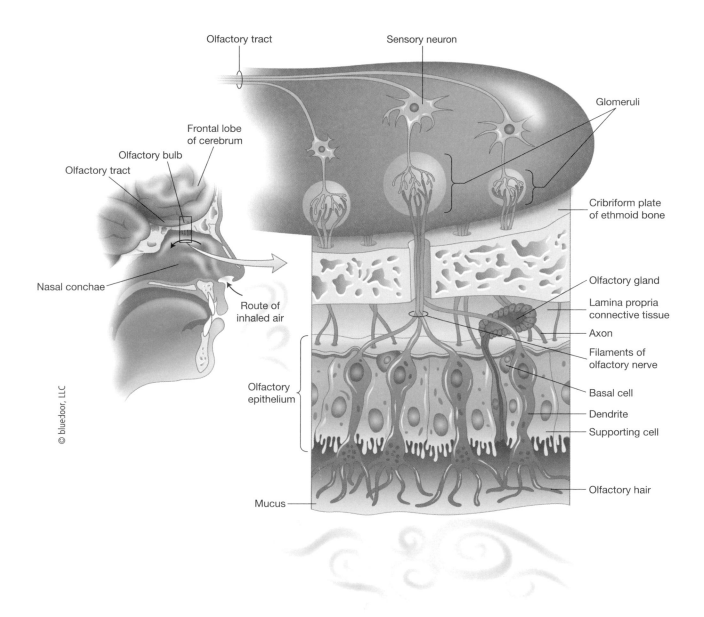

Figure 11.9: The nose and olfaction. The figure on the right is a magnified view of a section through the olfactory area in the nasal cavity and base of the brain.

Activity 11.8: Structures Associated with Olfaction

1. Study charts of the nose that are available in the lab.

2. Refer to charts in the lab and identify the following structures:

nose	olfactory cells	olfactory tract
nasal cavity	supporting cells	olfactory nerves
olfactory epithelium	olfactory bulb	

Activity 11.9: Olfaction

1. Follow the directions on the smell kit provided.

2. Place an unknown substance from the smell kit under your nose and identify the substance.

3. Repeat the procedure with two other unknown substances from the smell kit.

4. Circle the result of each smell test in the space below.

Results: Can you identify the substances? #1 Yes No   #2 Yes No   #3 Yes No

c) Taste Buds and Gustation

Taste buds are sensory receptors for gustation (taste). They are widely distributed on the posterior surface of the tongue. However, some are also found on the soft palate, the pharynx, and the cheeks. These are chemoreceptors that detect dissolved chemicals and generate action potentials. The taste buds are found within small peg-like projections known as **papillae** (Figure 11.10). Some people have more taste buds than others. Therefore, they are better tasters than others. Approximately 25% of people are non-tasters, 50% are average tasters, and the rest are superb tasters.

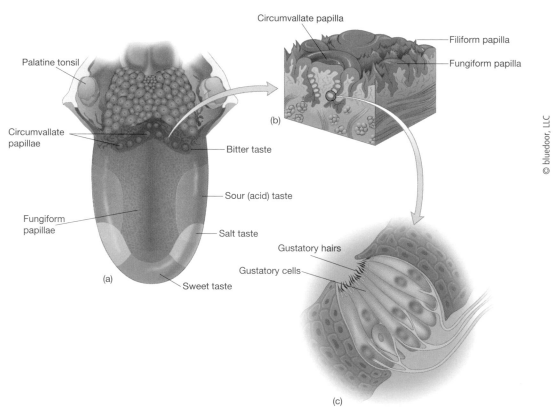

© bluedoor, LLC

Figure 11.10: Structures of gustation.
(a) Posterior surface of the tongue showing the average taste distributions and papillae.
(b) Magnified view of a section through papillae of the tongue. (c) Magnified view of a taste bud.

Activity 11.10: Taste Buds and Gustation

You may do this activity with your partner or individually by standing before a mirror.

Safety: Dispose of all materials that have made contact with bodily fluids in the biohazard container.

1. Obtain the following materials:
    *   Paper with a 7mm-wide hole
    *   A magnifying glass
    *   Blue food coloring
    *   A sterile cotton-tipped swab

2. Stand before a mirror and swab some blue food coloring onto the tip of your tongue. Note that the papillae of the tongue will remain pink.

3. Dispose of the swab in the biohazard container that is located near to the mirror.

4. Place the paper with the hole close to the front of your tongue and use the magnifying glass to enlarge the papillae that are visible through the hole. DO NOT TOUCH YOUR TONGUE WITH THE PAPER!

5. Count the number of visible papillae or ask your partner to count them for you. Note that non-tasters will have fewer than 15 visible papillae. Average tasters will have between 15 and 35 visible papillae. Superb tasters will have greater than 35 visible papillae.

6. Circle the number of counted papillae in the space provided.

Number of counted papillae: 0-15;   15-35;   >35

7. Are you a non-taster, average taster, or a superb taster? Circle your answer.

CHAPTER REVIEW

1. Which one of the following structures transmits sound waves to the middle ear?
    A. Auditory canal
    B. Tympanic membrane
    C. Incus
    D. Stapes

2. The component of a somatic reflex arc that is responsible for transmitting the action potential to the effector is called a/an _____.
    A. sensory receptor
    B. sensory neuron
    C. integration center
    D. motor neuron

3. Which one of the following cutaneous receptors detects painful mechanical stimuli?
   A. Merkel disc
   B. Nociceptors
   C. Meissner's corpuscle
   D. Pacinian corpuscle

4. Which one of the following structures contains the sensory receptors of hearing?
   A. Cochlea
   B. Semicircular canal
   C. Utricle
   D. Saccule

5. Neural hearing loss occurs when the _____ nerve is damaged.
   A. olfactory
   B. glossopharyngeal
   C. vagus
   D. vestibulocochlear

6. Which one of the following statements is **true**?
   A. Olfactory nerves pass through foramina in the cribriform plate.
   B. The dendrites of olfactory cells form the olfactory nerves.
   C. The axons form the olfactory hairs or cilia of chemoreceptors.
   D. The olfactory epithelium contains supporting cells only.

7. Which taste buds form a V shape configuration?
   A. fungiform
   B. filiform
   C. circumvallate
   D. foliate

8. Which one of the following is a cutaneous receptor that detects heavy touch stimuli?
   A. Merkel disc
   B. Nociceptor
   C. Meissner's corpuscle
   D. Pacinian corpuscle

9. Which one of the following structures is responsible for equalizing pressure?
   A. Auditory tube
   B. Tympanic membrane
   C. Incus
   D. Stapes

10. Which one of the following structures detects changes in head position and the force of gravity to allow the brain to distinguish the positions of the body?
    A. Cochlea
    B. Auditory canal
    C. Vestibule
    D. Oval window

Name: _____ Class Time: _____ Class Day: _____

Complete skill checks 1 – 3.

Skill check # 1

1. Name the reflex action that involves a rapid extension of the leg at the knee.

    _____

2. What are effectors?

    _____

3. What is a polysynaptic reflex?

    _____

Skill check # 2

1. Where are the hair cells for audition located?

    _____

2. What are Meissner's corpuscles?

    _____

3. Which receptors will be stimulated if your shoes are too small?

    _____

Skill check # 3

1. Name the two types of labyrinth in the inner ear.

    _____

2. What does the Weber test assess?

    _____

3. Where in the tongue are receptors that are sensitive to salt usually located?

    _____

12 Sensory System II: The Eye and Vision

OBJECTIVES:

After completing this laboratory you should be able to perform tasks listed below:

1. Identify the structures of the eye and describe their functions.
2. Perform physiological exercises related to vision.
3. Extrinsic muscles of the eye

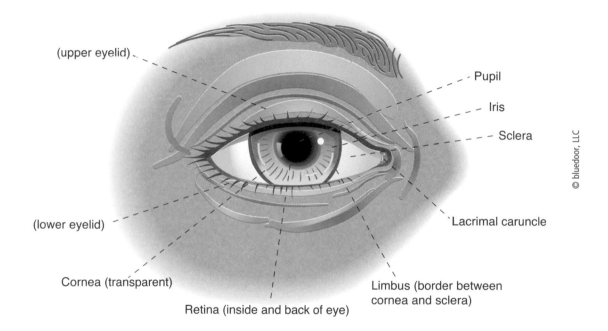

© bluedoor, LLC

Figure 12.1: The external eye

A. Accessory Eye Structures

Each eye is located in the orbit of the skull. Accessory structures that surround the eye facilitate support, protection, and movement.

Activity 12.1 Studying Accessory Eye Structures

1. Examine Figures 12.1, 12.2, 12.3 a, b and c as well as other illustrations of the human eye on charts in the lab.

2. Locate the following accessory eye structures on charts, models, or on your lab partner.

The primary eye accessory structures include:

Eyebrows: the fringe of hair superior to each orbit.

Eyelids: covering for the eye, it's composed of an outer layer of skin and an inner layer of mucous membrane.

Eyelashes: the small hairs attached to the eyelid.

Conjunctiva (conjunct = to meet): mucous membrane that covers the inside of the eyelid and the white part of the eyeball (sclera).

Lacrimal gland (Lacrimal = tears): the gland that produces tears, it's found superior and lateral to the eye.

Lacrimal canal: this medial canal drains tears into the nasal cavity.

Extrinsic eye muscles: six skeletal muscles that are attached external to the eye that provides eye movement.

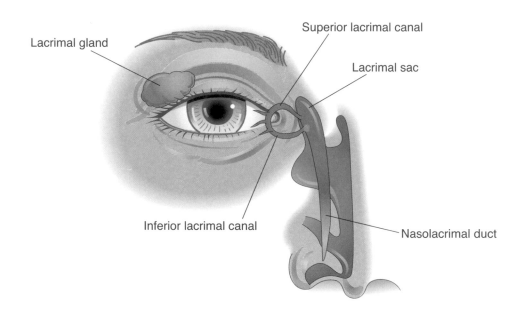

© bluedoor, LLC

Figure 12.2: The lacrimal apparatus

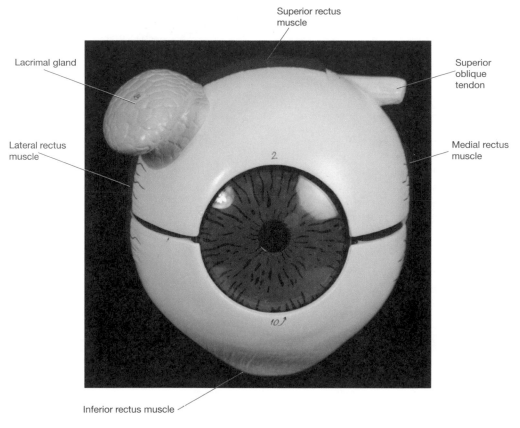

Figure 12.3a: Eye model, frontal view

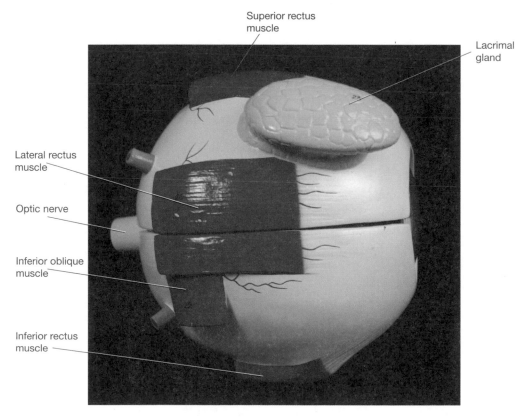

Figure 12.3b: Eye model, lateral view

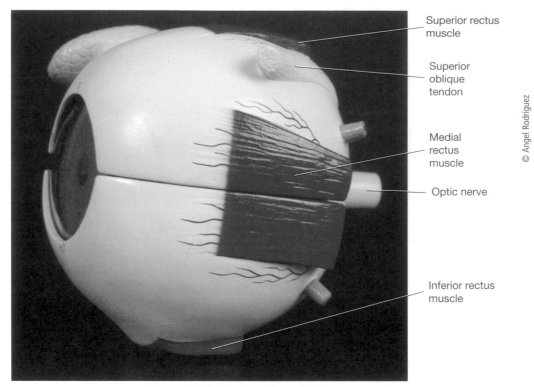

© Angel Rodriguez

Superior rectus muscle

Superior oblique tendon

Medial rectus muscle

Optic nerve

Inferior rectus muscle

Figure 12.3c: Eye model, medial view

B. Anatomy of the Eye

Activity 12.2 Studying Eye Anatomy

Find the following parts of the eye on the eye model provided:

Cornea (*cor* = **pupil**): the clear anterior part of the eye that covers the iris and pupil.

Sclera (*sclera* = **hard**): the white of the eye (outermost tunic).

Iris (*iris* = **rainbow**): the colored circle of the eye

Pupil: the black opening in the center of the iris – pupil diameter is controlled by the smooth muscle of the iris in response to light

Ciliary (*cili* = **hair**) **body:** a structure arising at the junction of the cornea and sclera

Ciliary muscle: a circular arrangement of smooth muscle in the ciliary body that alters the shape of the lens

Suspensory ligaments: attachments from the ciliary muscle to the lens

Choroid (*choroid* = **resembling a membrane**): middle tunic of the posterior part of the eye and it lines the interior of the sclera (between sclera and retina).

Retina (*ret* = **net**): the inner layer of the posterior eyeball, which contains the sensory receptors sensitive to light (photoreceptors).

Macula lutea (*macula* = **spot** + *lutea* = **yellow**): a region of the retina that has the highest visual acuity (sharpness of vision).

Optic disc (also called the Blind spot): the area of the retina that marks the exit of the optic nerve.

Lens: The lens is a transparent disc that serves to focus images on the retina.

Aqueous humor (*aqueous* = **watery** + *humor* = **fluid**): fluid that flows around the lens from the anterior chamber to the posterior chamber, it's continually recycled.

Vitreous humor (*vitreous* = **glassy** + *humor* = **fluid**) found in the posterior cavity. It helps to maintain the shape of the eye.

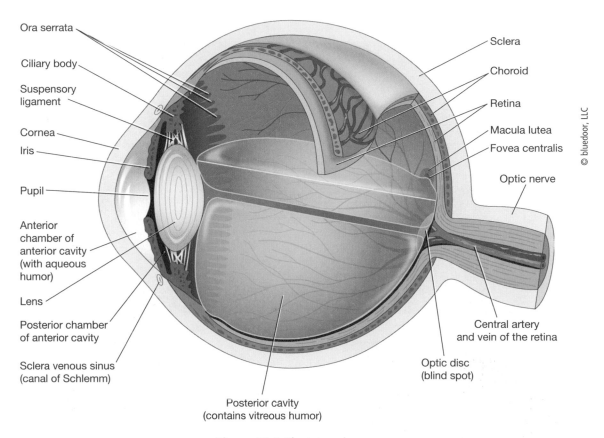

Figure 12.4: The internal eye

C. Dissection of the Preserved Cow's Eye

Activity 12.3: Dissection of the Preserved Cow Eye

**All students are required to adhere to the following
safety rules when handling the preserved eyes.**

Safety Rules:
- Wear disposable gloves, safety goggles, and a lab coat.
- Dispose of the dissected eyes in the biohazard container.
- Wash, disinfect, and dry the dissection equipment.
- Disinfect and dry the table tops with paper towel.
- Wash your hands thoroughly with soap and warm water after this activity.

1. Obtain a pairs of gloves, a pair of goggles, a dissection tray, and a dissection kit containing a scalpel and a blunt probe.
2. Put on your gloves and goggles.
3. Obtain a cow's eye from the container.
4. Wash the eye thoroughly with tap water to remove preservative.
5. Place the washed eye on your dissecting tray.

6. Refer to Figure 12.5(a) and identify the following external eye structures: **sclera**, **cornea**, **optic nerve**. <u>Show the external structures to you instructor before you cut the eye.</u>

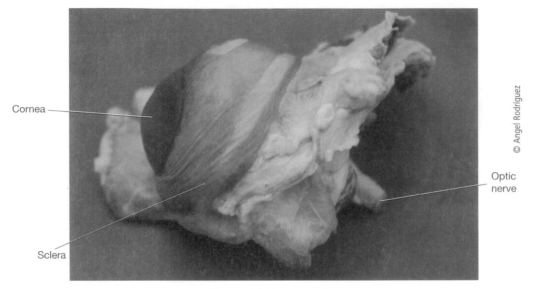

Figure 12.5a: External cow eye

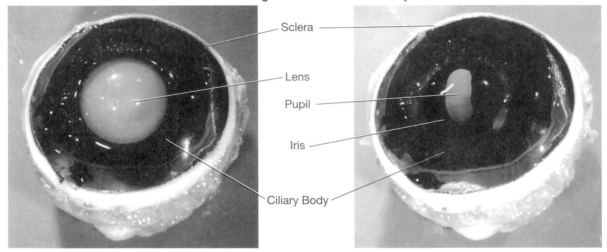

Figure 12.5b: Internal eye, anterior view

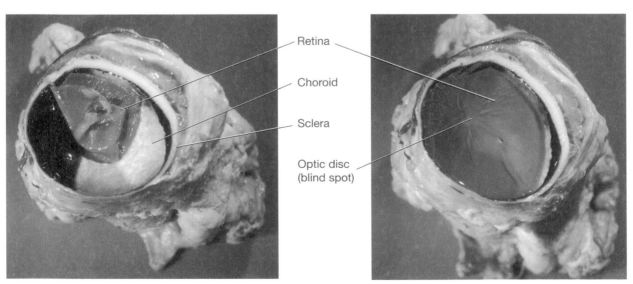

Figure 12.5c: Internal cow eye, posterior view

7. Place the eye on the posterior surface in the dissecting tray.
8. Place the tray in a sink before you cut the eye.
9. Ensure that the anterior surface of the eye is on top. Then, carefully use your scalpel to cut the eye straight across the middle like you would cut a bagel. **Do not put too much pressure on the eye when you make your initial cut because the aqueous and vitreous humor will squirt out of the eye.**
10. Examine the internal anatomy of the eye.
11. Refer to Figure 12.4 and find the following structures: lens, ciliary body, iris, and pupil.

D. Physiology of the Eye

Activity 12.4: Testing for Visual Acuity

You will use the **Snellen eye chart** in the lab to perform a simple test for visual acuity on your partner. Note that the left of side of the chart has numbers.

- A reading of 20/20 means that at 20 feet the person is reading what a person with normal vision should read.
- A reading of 20/40 indicates the person can see at 20 feet what someone with normal vision sees at 40 feet. Therefore, the person is nearsighted, or myopic.
- A reading of 20/15 is better than normal, because the subject sees at 20 feet what someone with normal vision sees at 15 feet.

1. Instruct your partner to stand 20 feet from the Snellen eye chart, and cover one eye with his or her hand.
2. Point to each line of letters on the chart and ask your partner to read the letters out loud. Be sure to start with the larger letters and move down to the smaller letters.
3. Record the fractional number on the left side of the line with the smallest letters that all can be read correctly.
4. Repeat the procedure with the other eye.
5. Record your results on the following lines:

Results:

Visual acuity of right eye without glasses:

_____

Visual acuity of left eye without glasses:

_____

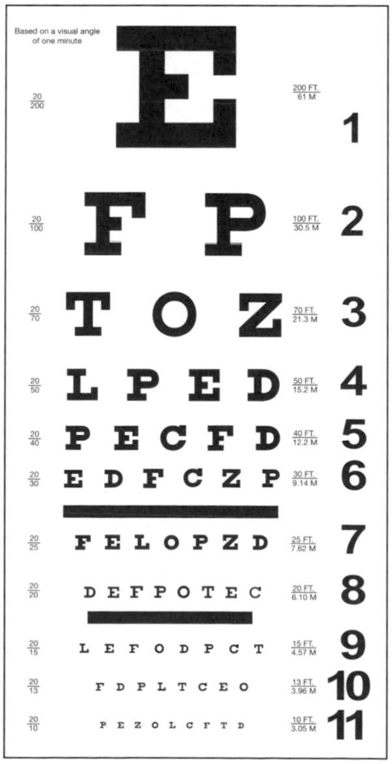

Figure 12.6: The Snellen chart

Activity 12.5: Testing for Astigmatism

You are required to test your lab partner's right and left eyes separately for astigmatism. **Astigmatism** (*a* = without + *stigma* = a mark)**:** A condition in which the curvature of the cornea is uneven, causing a blurring of vision. This happens because light does not focus clearly at one mark on the retina.

1. Let your lab partner take off glasses if they are being worn and then cover the right eye securely with one hand.
2. Let him or her view the astigmatism chart (Figure 12.7) with the left eye.
3. Find out from your partner if all spokes of the wheel are the same shade of dark black. Alternatively, find out which of the spokes, if any, appear darker then others.
4. Record the results.
5. Test your partner's right eye for astigmatism by repeating steps 2 & 3 with the left eye closed.

Is astigmatism present in the right eye? _____

Is astigmatism present in the left eye? _____

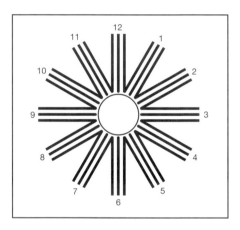

Figure 12.7: A chart to detect Astigmatism

© bluedoor, LLC

Activity 12.6: Detecting the Blind Spot

The blind spot corresponds to the optic disc where no vision is possible. Everyone one has a blind spot. In this simple exercise, you will find the blind spot in your visual field.

1. Cover your left eye and use your right eye to look at the black box in Figure 12.8. The circle should be in a lateral position.
2. Move the page with the figure forwards to about 25 cm from your face. Then, slowly bring the page closer to your eye. At a particular distance, the black dot will disappear from your vision. Be sure to look at the square throughout the activity.
3. Notice that the black dot disappears but the green line does not. This is called visual filling. Even though there is no vision, your brain fills the line in for you!

Figure 12.8: The test for detecting the blind spot. Note: visual filling.

Activity 12.7: Testing for Color Blindness

The test for color blindness is called the **Ishihara test.**

Use the following chart or one provided by your instructor to test your lab partner for color blindness.

Ask your patient, "What numbers do you see?" The correct answers are, "12, 8, 16 and 96."

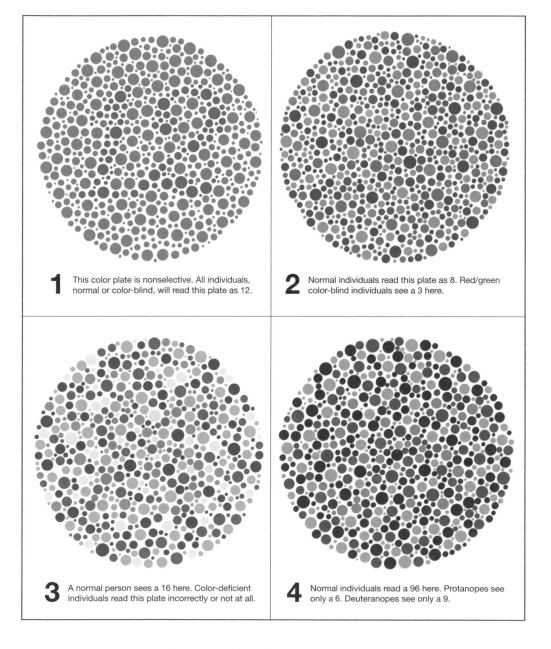

1 This color plate is nonselective. All individuals, normal or color-blind, will read this plate as 12.

2 Normal individuals read this plate as 8. Red/green color-blind individuals see a 3 here.

3 A normal person sees a 16 here. Color-deficient individuals read this plate incorrectly or not at all.

4 Normal individuals read a 96 here. Protanopes see only a 6. Deuteranopes see only a 9.

Figure 12.9: The Ishihara Color Blind Test

Activity 12.8: The Ophthalmological Exam

Figure 12.10: The Ophthalmological exam

The light intensity wheel of an ophthalmoscope is found on the upper part of the handle of the instrument. Rotation of the black wheel turns the light on and off. Rotation of the clear diopter wheel that is located on the side of the ophthalmoscope will allow you to see deep into your partner's eye.

1. Use your right eye to look into your partner's right eye and visa versa. **Please do not kiss your partner!**
2. Place your index finger on the diopter wheel of the ophthalmoscope.
3. Shine the light of the ophthalmoscope into your partner's eye so you can see the red reflex.
4. Start on "0" and rotate the diopter wheel with your index finger until you can see the entire area from your partner's lens to the retina.

CHAPTER REVIEW

1. What is the mucous membrane that covers the white of the eye called?

   _____

2. Why is the lacrimal gland located superior and lateral to the eye? _____

   _____

3. Macula degeneration affects the macula lutea. What effect does this disease have on vision?

   _____

4. Why is no vision possible when light focuses on the optic disc? _____

   _____

5. When you detected your blind spot, your brain filled in the green line. Why?

    _____

6. What would happen if you were to lose you aqueous humor?

    _____

7. What does it mean if you have 20/20 vision, as measured from the Snellen chart?

    _____

8. What is the cause of astigmatism?

    _____

9. What visual problem does a person with astigmatism experience?

    _____

10. Name the fluid that occupies the anterior chamber of the eye.

    _____

Name: _____Class Time: _____Class Day: _____

Complete skill checks 1 – 3.

Skill check #1

Point out and name the external parts of the cow's eye to your instructor before you cut the eye. Then, identify specific internal structures for your instructor.

Skill check #2

Study the eye model provided. Be prepared to identify the structures of the eye for your instructor.

Skill check #3

Be familiar with the eye tests that you performed today. Be able to perform each test and be prepared to answer your instructor's questions about the tests.